COGNITIVE NEUROSCIENCE

Nicole Fiori

Professor of Neuroscience
University of Paris V - René Descartes

PHI Learning Private Limited

New Delhi-110001
2010

Rs. 175.00

COGNITIVE NEUROSCIENCE
Nicole Fiori

The text is the translation of *Les neurosciences cognitives*.

Translator: Latha Anantharaman

Ouvrage publié avec le concours financier du National du Livre - Ministère français de la culture

The book is published with the financial aid of Centre National du Livre - French Ministry of Culture.

Published by arrangement with Armand Colin, 21 rue du Montparnasse 75006 Paris, France.

ISBN-978-81-203-4037-4

For sale in India, Pakistan, Bangladesh, Bhutan, Nepal, Sri Lanka and Maldives only.

The export rights of this book are vested solely with the publisher.

Published by Asoke K. Ghosh, PHI Learning Private Limited, M-97, Connaught Circus, New Delhi-110001 and Printed by Jay Print Pack Private Limited, New Delhi-110015.

Contents

Preface

This work is designed for the use of students taking their bachelor's degree or first year master's degree in psychology. It is a short handbook, limited to basic concepts and essential results in the field of cognitive neuroscience, useful for any student of psychology. Limited to cognitive neuroscience, that is, to the cerebral bases of cognition, it does not cover the entire programme of the bachelor's degree in neuroscience. Moreover, all aspects of cognition are not addressed.

Students of psychology, mainly having a background of training in literature, generally discover on their entry into university that the psychology that they will study is not the psychology of popular magazines and that it has a scientific basis. Some of them, having come to psychology because of an interest in clinical psychology, do not understand why they must nevertheless study psychophysiology and neuroscience. We hope that this small book will help them understand that they cannot practise psychology without working on the brain and without knowing a basic minimum about its functioning.

Students are also sometimes discouraged when they start discussing molecules, cells, and brain. The vocabulary of cognitive neuroscience may seem strange to those who are not used to it. As for the non-scientific undergraduates, it is true that we use many new words with which they are not immediately familiar. To remember the various structures of the brain is not easy when one does not regularly discuss them. Here also, we hope that this short handbook will be helpful.

The complexity of cognition makes it difficult to present the concepts. In fact, it is impossible to escape dividing it into functions (high-level perception, language, memory, attention) that are conventional and at the same time useful. But such a division is necessarily artificial. These major functions are all linked among themselves: perception and memory, perception and attention, language and memory, and so on. In any case, the presentation of this handbook corresponds to this mostly conventional division.

Following a historical account of research on the brain (Chapter 1), the organization of the nervous system is presented in Chapter 2, at the microscopic level (cell) and then at the macroscopic level (the principal structures of the brain). It is impossible to consult chapters on major functions if Chapter 2 is not properly understood. In fact, the discussion of cerebral structures throughout this work presupposes that the reader has a correct overall view of their location (presented in Chapter 2). This is why the principles or bases of brain anatomy have been summarized (at the end of the chapter) in order to facilitate cross-reference with subsequent chapters. Chapter 3 is devoted to the major principles of methods of brain imaging. Here also, we have sought to make it simple for the student to remember the essentials. The specialist of these methods will find some gaps here. However, the student in psychology is not a specialist but generally has an approximate understanding and the aim is to improve the student's understanding of the differences between these various methods: their principles and what they allow us to measure, and their respective advantages and disadvantages.

The subsequent chapters are focused on major functions: high-level perception (Chapter 4), memory (Chapter 5), language (Chapter 6), and attention (Chapter 7). In each of the chapters 4 through 8, there is thus a summary presentation of models of cognitive psychology. We decided in Chapter 8 to touch on hemispheric specialization (right brain and left brain) and the question of differences between the male and the female brain. This question is always difficult to tackle to the extent that inter-individual differences are always subject to abusive interpretation and use. Between those who affirm that there is no difference between males and females in the name of equality and those who draw from possible differences justifications for social inequalities, it appears best to us to expose what is known. It is seen that the data that are available are quite fragmented and, in any case, there is no room to draw from them any justification for unequal treatment or consideration of men and women. Nothing suggests that men are superior to women (which many already doubt) but nothing suggests the contrary either!

Finally, Chapter 9 is devoted to the relationships between emotion and cognition. The current of research linking these two subjects is recent and has not reached a consensus. Moreover, the available data are still scarce. It seems, however, useful to address this new advance, which could contribute greatly to the constitution of new understanding and a certain bringing together of sub-disciplines of psychology that have so far been quite distant (such as clinical psychology and cognitive psychology) in terms of methods as well as subjects.

I am grateful to Nicole Bacri, who proposed the compilation of this handbook. Her open mind always enforced the need for a solid foundation of neuroscience for psychologists. It is therefore not surprising that she has wished that a handbook of cognitive neuroscience would figure in the coursework designed for students of psychology. That she chose me to carry out this task is an honour. I also thank the many students on whom I tried out the contents of this handbook in the course of my undergraduate and graduate education. My interaction with them was very profitable to me. I thank my colleagues Eric Sieroff and Laurence Chaby, who helped me to find certain images and scientific articles, and more generally were lavish with advice during our numerous discussions on our respective subjects. I also thank Nassim Medjahed, who refined some of my illustrations in order to render them presentable. Finally, I thank Pierre Duharcourt, whose attentive reading of this manuscript and remarks made it possible to correct faults, confused expressions and awkwardness of style, even though some of these are sure to remain.

Nicole Fiori

1

Cognitive Neuroscience

The objective of this work is to discuss the higher mental (cognitive) functions from the perspective of brain function.

The term *cognitive neuroscience* is recent (just about 30 years old). Even today, it is contested by some schools of thought, which prefer to preserve the slightly older term *neuroscience*. Others talk of *neurobiology* or *neurophysiology*. Some still claim the term *psychophysiology*. The picture would not be complete without the term *neuropsychology*. These debates are of no interest to the student of psychology and, if only for this reason, we will not enter into the argument here. We simply seek to clarify these terms (which the student will encounter to some extent) by giving succinct definitions. Subsequently, we review some major stages in brain research.

1.1 SOME DEFINITIONS

Neuroscience, as the name indicates, relate to the science of neurons and the nervous system. But neuronal function can be studied at several levels. Some concepts become clear when one fine-tunes the level of analysis at which one works.

The most elementary level of brain function is that of the molecules that allow neurons to communicate with each other. This is called *molecular neurobiology* or *molecular neuroscience.*

The next level is that of the cell. In the case of the brain, this refers again to the neuron but also to the glial cells. This is called *neurobiology* or *cellular neuroscience.*

The next level is the domain of integration. The neurons constituting complex networks form integrated systems such as the visual system. The term used is *integrated neuroscience* (some use the term *integrative neuroscience*).

Cognitive neuroscience pertains to mechanisms of the most complex neuronal systems, associated with higher mental functions (such as language, memory, or attention as well as conscience, mental representations). We may ask, therefore, what differentiates cognitive neuroscience from neuropsychology. In fact, according to Hécaen (1972), the founding father of modern neuropsychology, neuropsychology is related to the study of higher functions linked with cerebral structures. Hécaen's definition of neuropsychology is not the only one. It must be recalled that, overall, beyond the subtleties of definition, the object of the neuropsychologist's study is the brain-damaged patient. Having located the lesion and affected brain structures, the neuropsychologist "deduces" from the problems observed in a given cognitive function the cerebral structures implicated in that function. Cognitive neuroscience more often uses data collected from animals and, in humans, data from the application of methods of brain imaging (without neglecting those collected from the study of brain-damaged patients).

Psychophysiology, etymologically, is the study of the physiological bases of the mind. In fact, it is not possible to separate the definition of psychophysiology from its context, where the mind is studied by strict behavioural scientists. In other words, psychophysiology involves the behaviour of an animal in its environment, a human being seen as a particular animal. Of course, the term *behaviour* itself has many definitions. However, without venturing again into controversy, it is possible to say that a behaviour is a set of phenomena, acts, and reactions, observable externally, to the promptings of the environment. If the nervous system is obviously the object of the study of physiological bases of its behaviours, the question arises afresh of the level of analysis at which one operates. In reality, the reduction of the mind to behaviour can obviously be bypassed to include cognition. This is a step that is not taken by all.

In fact, definitions must also refer to methods used and the subject of study (animal or humans).

Many results acquired in the domain of neuroscience have been and still are taken from the study of animals. This poses at least two problems. The first is scientific. It is in fact never certain whether the results acquired from a study of animals can be extrapolated to humans, while it is true that humans are considerably more complex than any animal, even the most evolved. Moreover, depending on the subject of the research, there will be an interest in experimenting on one or another animal, depending on the possible similarities of function between that animal and humans. In any case, it can safely be affirmed that any knowledge gained about humans has been acquired only from prior animal experimentation. In the rest of this work, we will refer often to data collected about animals. The second problem with animal experimentation is ethical. For a long time, humans have considered animals to be at their disposal, and the suffering of animals was ignored, even denied. Fortunately, animals are now protected and animal experimentation is restricted by legislation (at least in many developed countries). It is practised only when it is necessary to advance science and when no other method is possible; the animals must not suffer before or during the experiment. Although mass media does reveal abuses and violation of such regulation, cases remain rare.

With respect to the methods, they relate to *in vitro* experimentation practices[1] in cellular or molecular neurobiology with the brain imaging practised in cognitive neuroscience (which is discussed in Chapter 3). Between these two extremes, neurophysiologists stimulate or record electrical activity of some neurons of a cerebral structure by a micro-electrode implanted in the brain of the animal. We will see in the rest of this work that, in some pathologies, this method is applied to humans for therapeutic purposes. We find also the post-mortem autopsies of neuro-anatomists. In brief, methods are diverse with respect to the object of study, from the most simple to the most integrated.

Our knowledge of cerebral function underlying cognition, the subject of cognitive neuroscience, relies thus on data derived from these various processes. The data collected from animals often serve as a basis: then researchers seek to verify whether they can be extrapolated to humans. But this is not the only thing. Scientists also rely on data from neuropsychology and psychology. Psychology, with its behavioural methods, elaborates models

---

[1] *In vitro* experiments consist of experiments on an element taken from an animal, as when a science teacher at school takes the nerve and muscle from a frog's leg, stimulates them with an electric shock and asks students to observe what happens to the muscle.

of cognitive function that are generally the basis of research in cognitive neuroscience. The study of cerebral function thus allows us to confirm, invalidate, and enrich these models. There is thus feedback between the models elaborated by these two disciplines, all contributing to the enrichment of our understanding of cognitive functioning. It is, moreover, interesting to note that in the United States, researchers in cognitive psychology, neuropsychology and cognitive neuroscience are affiliated generally with the same research laboratories. Gazzaniga, Posner and other authors rely more on cognitive psychology than on cognitive neuroscience. In France, we will not achieve the same advances if these disciplines are not more promptly brought closer.

To conclude this question of definitions, a word must be said about cognitive sciences. It is a still vast discipline that integrates highly diverse procedures and methods. In this field there are psychologists and neuroscientists, of course, but also philosophers and statisticians, whose disciplines have in common that they base their specific knowledge on the cognitive functioning of humans, allowing advancement in their understanding of that functioning.

1.2 BRIEF HISTORY OF BRAIN RESEARCH

From ancient times to a relatively recent period, it was the heart that was considered the seat of thought, the soul. Nevertheless, from prehistoric times (5000 BC), it seems that trepanning, for therapeutic purposes (but why, no one knows), has been carried out on the brain. At least, this is cited by those who study human skulls exhumed and now displayed in museums. Similarly, there are inscriptions on papyrus dating from this epoch, in which the doctors of ancient Egypt made the link between the appearance of certain problems and a breaking open of the skull at such a point, thus opening a route very different from the neuropsychology of today. Nevertheless, the death rites of the time testify that the brain was not considered an essential element of man, since the body was embalmed and preserved after extraction of the brain.

In ancient Greece, in the 6th century BC, Alcmaeon of Croton (a doctor who was a disciple of Pythagoras) inaugurated the experimental method in biology by dissecting cadavers and by animal vivisection and distinguished veins from arteries. But, in working also on relationships between the visual function and the brain, he seemed also to be the first to have affirmed that the seat of governance is the brain. It is thus the thesis of Alcmaeon of Croton that was taken up a century later by Hippocrates

(460-379 BC), who advanced that the brain is implicated in sensations and was the seat of intelligence, a thesis also stated by Plato (427-348 BC). Nevertheless, Aristotle (384-332 BC) contested these theses, maintaining that the heart was the seat of sensation and intelligence.

Under the Roman Empire, a major step was taken by Claudius Galen in the 2nd century (around 131-201 AD) with the description of nerves (which he compared to canals) and their influence on the muscles and on movement. Above all, he presented the first descriptions of the brain, the cerebellum, and the ventricles (the hollow spaces at the centre of the brain). For Galen, four liquids (humours) presided over the corporal functions. These humours flowed along nerves (perceived as canals) either towards or away from the ventricles and it was these flows that caused movements.

During the Renaissance (16th century AD), advances were made in anatomy with the well-documented drawings and illustrations of Leonardo da Vinci (1452-1519) and the works of Andreas Vesalius (1514-1564) on the anatomy of the body and brain. Galen's conception of flows of humours was not questioned.

Thus we come to René Descartes (1596-1650), philosopher, physician and mathematician. He did not question Galen's conception for animals but do so for humans. More precisely, he considered that human behaviour similar to that of animals was effectively the result of flows of humours through ventricles, but that humans had more spirit (a soul given by God) than did animals, which could not be due to the same mechanisms. For Descartes, the mental faculties of man arose from the spirit and not from the body. The brain was part of the body, the spirit was something else. The spirit received sensations, it governed movements and communication with the brain, in a way charged with the execution of what the spirit commanded. Having remarked that the structures of the brain, identified by anatomists, were all double, with the exception of the pineal gland, a small gland located at the centre of the brain and today called epiphysis, Descartes believed that the spirit communicated with the brain through the pineal gland.[2] The separation delineated by Descartes between body and spirit was referred to as "Descartes' Error" by Damasio (1994) in his celebrated work of the same title. Note that the debate over the separation of body and spirit is still not closed. Since the mental functions are far from being elucidated, even though cognitive neuroscience (and other fields) is yoked to the task and attempt to refine the supporting data, the mystery of the

---

[2] The pineal gland or epiphysis is known today for its role in the production of melatonin, a hormone essential to the biological clock.

formation of thought in humans is far from being resolved and this is the reason some continue to conceive of thought in immaterial terms.

Subsequently (in the 18th and 19th centuries), technological progress made possible advances in anatomy: Galen's theory was abandoned, and the nervous system was described in its entirety. De la Mettrie (1709-1751) eliminated the notion of soul: he considered the body (including the brain) thenceforth as a whole that resembled a machine. The discoveries by anatomists of the relationships between the brain and nerves multiplied and gave rise, at the same time, to philosophical reflections: Diderot (1713-1784) compared the brain to a spider whose web is made up of nerves.

F.J. Gall (1758-1828) was the first to advance a theory of the location of cerebral functions, designated *phrenology*. Gall believed that the bumps on the cranium, which can be detected by touch, corresponded to cerebral convolutions and that each of them corresponded to a function or rather to a personality trait. He claimed to detect 27 bumps corresponding to the sites of emotionality, imitation, astonishment, aggression, etc. Phrenology launched a violent controversy: scientists, particularly anatomists who "knew" the brain (e.g., Flourens, 1794-1867), contested Gall's thesis on the following bases: (1) the form of the cranium does not reflect the structure of the brain, (2) lesions in a particular region of the brain do not lead to problems linked to characters itemized by Gall on the cranium, and also (3) all the regions of the brain were equally implicated in any function. Although the first two arguments were true, history shows that their unitary vision of brain function was erroneous. Phrenology seems today so naïve that one may ask why it is included in this history of brain research. In fact, it is necessary to situate it in the context of the time. Beyond its gross errors (the traces of which are unfortunately still perceptible in beliefs such as that in "math bumps"), Gall had an ingenious intuition in representing the brain as a whole with localized functions.

Discoveries by Broca (1824-1880) and then Wernicke (1848-1904) of the kinds of aphasia that are named for them, associated with a lesion of the frontal lobe (Broca's aphasia) and the temporal lobe (Wernicke's aphasia), marked the true beginnings of the concept of localization of cerebral functions. We must also cite, in the same thread, the description by Harlow, in 1848, of a patient (Phineas Gage) injured in the anterior part of the frontal lobe, whose personality changed fundamentally even while his intellectual faculties seemed intact.

Of course, we must cite here the theory of evolution of Charles Darwin (1809-1892), who, in postulating in 1859 in his work *On the Origin of Species* a development of species (and thus their brain) from a common ancestor, opened up the way for research on animals, the results of which could be extrapolated to humans. Moreover, the association between the specific behaviours of certain species and particular developments of certain parts of their brain make it possible to fine-tune the anatomy of the brain with respect to these behaviours.

The progress achieved meanwhile in microscope technology and cell staining allowed Golgi (1835-1909), Ramón y Cajal (1852-1934) and Sherrington (1857-1952) to distinguish various sorts of cells and neurons by their forms, properties, functions and connections. Thus, after the representation in 1850 by Leuret and Gratiolet of the spinal cord, the bulb and the cerebral trunk, the two hemispheres and the callous bodies, it was Brodmann who established in 1909 the first detailed map of the human brain. The 52 areas identified by Brodmann have been demarcated by means of the architecture of the nerve cells. From that time, the anatomy of the brain has been formulated along these general lines.

Curiously, the scientific advances introduced by behavioural trends in psychology in the early 20th century with the works of Watson (1913) helped mark a step in research on cognitive function. On the one hand, in studying only observable behaviours, objectives, and individuals in their relationship to the environment, behaviourism allowed experimental psychology to achieve an introspective advance of mental processes, emotions and sentiments. It allowed it to acquire the status of a science along with other natural sciences. The contribution of behaviourism to the study of human behaviour is immense. Its applications are multiple whether in the domain of methods of education and foundation or in the therapeutic domain with the implementation of behavioural therapies particularly adapted to certain behavioural problems. On the other hand, the reduction of research to observable behaviours has moved away from the scientific field of research on human thought in all its complexity, not flowing from a simple schema of responses determined by stimulations from the environment. In particular, the part of emotions in cognition has been totally obscured for a long time and is still a matter of controversy today (see Chapter 9).

Eventually, one can say that the introduction of concepts such as cognition, cognitive psychology, and cognitive neuroscience marks a novel approach to thought linked with its cerebral bases.

The course of the history of research on the brain, in the 20th and 21st centuries, is partly contained in the body of this work. Following the progress made possible by the electronic microscope in fine anatomy, the advent of methods of brain imaging is a virtual revolution for knowledge of matters of brain anatomy and especially for the study of brain function during the realization of cognitive tasks. The progress achieved over about 30 years has been immense. The complementarity of data and models of cognitive psychology and data from functional brain imaging undoubtedly make it possible to advance in great strides in the next few years. This will lead to a hope of understanding—and treating—certain pathologies. Important among such pathologies in terms of public health are Parkinson's disease and Alzheimer's disease, both of which result from degeneration of neurons in specific regions of the brain. We can also cite mental illnesses such as schizophrenia, which is presently the subject of a large number of studies in brain imaging showing a dysfunction of the frontal lobe that is expressed in diminished frontal activity to the benefit of a temporal hyperactivity and suggesting a flaw in connections between various cortical and sub-cortical regions.

Having said that, without wishing to conclude this introductory chapter on a note that may seem pessimistic, it seems necessary to slightly temper the enthusiasm generated by this new advance at least in its most exaggerated aspects. The richness and complexity of human thought are immense and constitute a formidable challenge to scientists. Nevertheless, it is probable that the discovery of all the mechanisms of human thought is not imminent. To ignore this may lead to false hopes and to errors from which the history of science is unhappily not exempt. Let us not forget, for example, that abusive and erroneous use of certain data about the brain has served the purposes of racist theses. No one can say that such abuses are no longer possible. It is in fact always possible to use average data to deduce from it the abnormality of an individual who deviates from the average.

2

Organization of the Nervous System

The organization of the nervous system can be seen from a "microscopic" or "macroscopic" point of view. The first point of view relates to the cell, or rather to the nerve tissue. The second refers to the major subdivisions of the nervous system in relation to its functioning.

This organization could in itself be the subject of a book, but that is not our objective here. Only the essentials are summarized.

2.1 MICROSCOPIC ORGANIZATION: THE NERVE TISSUE

The nerve tissue is made up of two major types of cells: nerve cells (or neurons, at a number presently estimated at 1 billion in a single brain) and glial cells (neuroglia or, more simply, glia), which are even more numerous. If neurons constitute the basic substrate of the transmission of nerve information, the glial cells are necessary to this transmission, even though they do not directly transmit this information.

It was Santiago Ramón y Cajal, a Spanish histologist contemporaneous with Sigmund Freud, who first showed that the cerebral tissue is organized into discrete functional units, free and clearly separated (the neurons), a discovery for which he received the Nobel Prize in 1906 with his colleague

Camillo Golgi. At the same time, based notably on the observation of a space separating the neurons, he put forth the hypothesis of a chemical mode of communication between these units.

2.1.1   Neurons

Neurons are excitable cells of the nervous system that carry information between the periphery and the central nervous system and, reciprocally, between the various regions of the central nervous system. They are thus the basic cells that allow an organism to receive information about the environment and act on this environment, as well as to think, memorize, anticipate, programme an action, and so on.

The conventionally described neuron (Fig. 2.1) comprises a cellular body (or soma), lengthened on one side by dendrites (short extensions) and on the other side by an axon (long extension). The axon itself is divided, at its end, into fine branches (axonal ramifications or synaptic terminations). This is a very particular cell that is excitable and at the same time secretory. In fact, the neuron can transmit and propagate information that it receives in the form of electrical impulses along its axon (designated *nervous influx*) and liberate, at the end of its axonal ramifications, chemical molecules (neurotransmitters), which are captured, at the level of dendrites of the post-synaptic neuron, by specific chemical receptors.

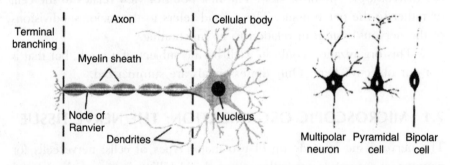

Fig. 2.1 The neuron. Left: diagram of the different parts of a neuron. Right: different types of neurons (multipolar neuron, pyramidal cell, bipolar cell).

The cell body is demarcated by a membrane, made up of a double lipid layer, which encloses a nucleus and the elements necessary to the cell[1] (endoplasmic reticulum, ribosomes, Golgi apparatus, mitochondria), the whole bathed in cytoplasm, an intracellular liquid common to all cells of the body.

---

[1] Recall that the nucleus and mitochondria contain the genetic inheritance, mitochondrial DNA being different from and complementary to nuclear DNA.

In fact, there are several types of neurons that differ in their morphology, that is, by their soma and, more particularly, their extensions (dendrites and axons, which are called "neuritis"). Generally, the neurons of the same form have the same functional properties and are found in large number in a single region of the nervous system. This does not mean that in such a particular region of the nervous system there are only neurons of a single type, but that these are in the vast majority. The morphology of neurons thus constitutes one of the elements making it possible to identify and distinguish the different regions of the nervous system. It is, moreover, linked to the "treatment" that the neuron performs. For example, the long axons authorize rapid transmission of information, without loss or modification, since there is no synapse over a large distance. But the functioning of these long extensions requires a large quantity of nutrients that must be furnished by the soma. This is why, generally, neurons in which the cell body is voluminous have long extensions that carry information to distant regions, as is the case, for example, of the larger spinal motoneurons.

If one looks at the extensions, three major categories of neurons (Fig. 2.1) can be cited, even though these categories can themselves be broken down into subcategories.

1. The multipolar neurons correspond to the neuron described previously, with an axon and dendrites. This is the case, for example, in vertebrates, with most of the neurons of the brain. Note, however, that all neurons—multipolar—of the brain are not of identical form. For example, at the cortex, the large pyramidal cells, in which the shape of the soma is reminiscent of a cone or pyramid and the principal dendrite is directed towards the surface while the axon is directed toward the white matter, differ from the starred cells whose cell body and axon are smaller and in which the dendritic branching extends on the entire surface of the cell body, thus giving to the cell a starry appearance. The Purkinje cells of the cerebellum and the motoneurons constitute still other sorts of multipolar neurons present in the nervous system.

2. The bipolar neurons have two extensions of nearly equal length (one axon and one dendrite) ending in ramifications. These neurons are typical enough of sensory systems (e.g., the layer of bipolar cells in the retina).

3. The pseudo-monopolar neurons of the nervous system of vertebrates are the equivalent of monopolar neurons of invertebrates: a single extension starts from the soma (the axon). It extends in two directions, along an axonal pole and a dendritic pole.

One can also classify the neurons by size: small cells (stars, grains), and large cells (pyramidal cells, Purkinje cells).

Finally, neurons can be classified on the basis of their function: the afferent neurons, the efferent neurons, and the neurons of association or interneurons. The afferent or sensory neurons are bipolar or pseudo-monopolar. The efferent neurons cover, essentially, the large multipolar neurons that are the motoneurons. The neurons of association ensure liaisons between different regions of the central nervous system. They can thus have a more or less long axon, depending on the distance of the link. These interneurons constitute the most numerous category of neurons of the nervous system.

2.1.2 Synapse

The term *synapse* was proposed by Sherrington at the end of the 19th century (today, this term also designates the junction between the nerve and the muscle or the neuromuscular junction). The synapse is thus an element of junction between the neurons allowing the transmission of information (synaptic transmission). It is in fact a space between the pre-synaptic element (axonal ramifications) and the post-synaptic element (dendrites). The "dendrite–cell body" pole is the "receptor" part, while the "axon–axonal ramification" pole is the "emitting" part. Most synapses are chemical synapses in which a neurotransmitter (chemical molecule) is liberated by axonal ramifications—pre-synaptic element—in the synaptic space and fixed by receptors (also chemical) at the level of dendrites—post-synaptic elements.[2] A neurotransmitter is thus a chemical molecule that permits the nervous influx to pass from one neuron to the other. There are about 60 neurotransmitters presently listed, of which the chief ones are acetylcholine, serotonin, histamine, adenosine triphosphate (ATP), catecholamines (dopamine, adrenaline, noradrenaline), amino acids (glutamate and gamma-aminobutyric acid, commonly called GABA) as well as peptides and water-soluble gases such as nitrogen monoxide. Furthermore, it is important to know that neurotransmitters are sometimes exciters (e.g., glutamate) and thus favour the transmission of nervous influx from one neuron to another, and sometimes inhibitors (e.g., dopamine, GABA) and thus obstruct such transmission.

2.1.3 The Glial Cells (Glia)

The glia (from the Greek *glia*, which signifies glue) or neuroglia (neuron glue) ensures the support of nerve cells, acting as their glue, as well as their

---

[2] There are also electrical synapses in which the electric signals are transmitted directly from neuron to neuron without chemical intervention as well as mixed synapses.

nutrition. Unlike most nerve cells, the glial cells reproduce throughout their lifetime. There are four types of glial cells. All of them, in their way, participate in the proper functioning of neurons.

The astrocytes occupy most of the space between neurons in the neuronal tissue. Star-shaped, these cells are provided with numerous filaments in all directions, which come into contact with neurons, the blood capillaries of the brain, and the ependymal cells. By means of these contacts, the astrocytes allow exchanges between the neurons and the blood—the carrying of nutrients from the blood to the neurons and to the cephalo-rachidian liquid, the evacuation of wastes from the neurons towards the blood. The role of astrocytes is not limited to these exchanges. It also plays a role in the communication between neurons by intervening in the metabolism of neurotransmitters and in the regulation of the ionic equilibrium. Moreover, over the course of development of the nervous system in the embryo, the astrocytes guide cellular migrations along the neural tube and participate in the formation of the hemato-encephalic barrier. The functions of astrocytes are thus complex.

The microglia is constituted, as its name indicates, of very small cells that play a role in defence against viruses and bacteria susceptible of attacking and thus destroying neurons.

The oligodendrocytes roll around the axons of neurons of the central nervous system just as the Schwann cells do around the nerve fibres of the peripheral nervous system. It is these two types of cells that fabricate the myelin but, while one oligodendrocyte may myelinize several segments of axons, even several axons, a Schwann cell myelinizes only a portion of one axon. The myelin sheath thus formed around axons is not continuous: it is interrupted by spaces—nodes of Ranvier—where the axon is "bare" (Fig. 2.1). We will see that this myelin sheath, with its nodes of Ranvier, plays an important role in the rate of conduction of nervous influx by axons. The pathologies in which the myelin sheath is damaged (e.g., multiple sclerosis) are manifested in a slowing down, even interruption, of nerve conduction. Note that myelinization operates, for the most part, after birth, for the first 10 to 15 years of life, and that the axons of very small diameter have no such sheath. Finally, being made up of a double lipid layer, the myelin sheath lends a white colour to the axons that it surrounds (whence the name "white matter").

2.1.4 Other Cells

Apart from the cells ensuring the vascularization of the brain—see below—we must also mention the cells that have a protective role with respect to the nerve tissue. Some authors classify here the cells of the microglia and above all the ependymal cells, which cover the walls of cavities (ventricles and canals) enclosing the cephalo-rachidian liquid. They impede the passage of toxins into this liquid, which ensures the transport of nutrients to the neurons and the elimination of their wastes.

2.2 THE NERVE SIGNALS

The neurons are excitable and excretory cells. They communicate among themselves by the intermediary of synapses. The message carried from neuron to neuron is called *nervous influx*.

2.2.1 Neuron Membrane, Extracellular Medium, Intracellular Medium

The neuron is surrounded by a membrane (plasma membrane) composed of a double layer of lipid cells that separate the extracellular space (at the exterior of the neuron) from the intracellular space (the cytoplasm, inside the neuron). These two spaces are liquid media of different composition that are both conducting liquids. The lipidic composition of the membrane impedes what is dissolved by its media (since the lipids are not water-soluble) and the passage across the membrane of elements of these liquids: consequently, the double lipid layer of the membrane forms a barrier for the ions and proteins present in the extra- and intracellular mediums. Nevertheless, proteins are encrusted in the plasma membrane, which makes it possible to remain permeable, selectively, to certain ions that can thus cross under certain conditions. These proteins are designated as "canal proteins" or ionic canals: specific to certain ions, they allow only these ions to pass and not others. There are thus ionic canals specific to potassium (K^+ ions), sodium (Na^+) and calcium (Ca^{++}). Moreover, there are other specific proteins, also crossing the membrane, that form "ionic pumps". These are enzymes that use the energy supplied by hydrolysis of ATP molecules to "pump", that is, to make certain ions cross the membrane. The sodium-potassium pump is thus essential to the maintenance of the characteristic equilibrium of the neuron at rest.

2.2.2 Resting Potential

The composition of extra- and intracellular mediums is not the same because their chemical concentrations differ. The interior of the cell is more charged with K^+ ions charged positively and in negatively charged proteins while the exterior is more charged with Na⁺ ions charged positively and Cl⁻ ions (chlorine) charged negatively. But, even at rest, each ion tends to move under the effect of two mechanisms: on the one hand, it tends to go from the medium in which it is most present to the medium in which it is least present (the effect of its gradient of concentration); on the other hand, it tends to distance itself from a medium that contains charges (positive or negative) similar to its own to go towards a medium containing opposite charges. For example, K^+ ions, present in numbers in the interior, tend to leave the cell (to go toward the medium less concentrated in K^+ ions); on the other hand, by the inverse phenomenon, Na^+ ions tend to enter the cell. The sodium-potassium pump thus intervenes to re-balance these diffusions of ions, but it does it in the following manner: each time it expels three sodium ions from the interior to the exterior, it integrates only two potassium ions into the cell. Thus, it creates a difference in charge between the interior and exterior: the interior of the cell is charged negatively while the exterior is charged positively. The neuron is thus "polarized" (there are more positive charges outside than inside) and it behaves like an electric battery whose negative pole is inside and positive pole outside. This potential is on average –70 millivolts (mV) depending on the neurons; it varies from –60 to –80 mV. This is called the *resting potential* of the membrane.

2.2.3 Action Potential

Ionic canals open under the effect of a stimulation that is electric along the axon, chemical at the synaptic level (the stimulation thus emanates from a neurotransmitter released in the synaptic space).

When an excited neuron liberates its neurotransmitter in the synaptic space, that creates a small local variation of potential of the membrane at the dendrites or cell body of the post-synaptic neuron. But this does not necessarily lead to an excitation sufficient for the post-synaptic neuron in turn to transmit the information in the form of a nervous influx. A single post-synaptic neuron is connected to numerous pre-synaptic neurons. It is subject thus to excitatory influences and inhibitory influences that lead to movements of ions across the membrane of the post-synaptic neuron, some of which tend to increase the membrane potential (*hyperpolarization:* the membrane potential becomes still more negative) and some of which diminish it (*depolarization:* the membrane potential becomes less negative). In fact, for the post-synaptic neuron to itself transmit the excitation that it receives from a pre-synaptic neuron, it is necessary that its membrane potential vary greatly and reach at least –30 mV: the neuron is thus depolarized. This is the threshold value of the triggering of an action potential.

The action potential generated by the depolarization of the membrane of the soma of the neuron arises at the very beginning of the axon of this neuron. This action potential takes on several characteristics.

In the first place, the action potential follows the all-or-nothing law. As soon as the membrane potential reaches the critical threshold of -40 mV, an action potential is generated on the axon (see Fig. 2.2). Moreover, this action potential is always of equal amplitude. This is thus an inversion of the polarity of the membrane of the axon, which becomes positive (thus going from a resting potential of -70 mV to a potential of +30 mV), a phenomenon that lasts only two or three milliseconds. Once it is generated, the action potential is propagated at very high speed all along the axon, without losing its intensity. Finally, the passage of the action potential is followed to the extent that it is displaced along the axon, by a short refractory period during which the membrane is no longer stimulated, which hinders the "recoil" of the action potential.

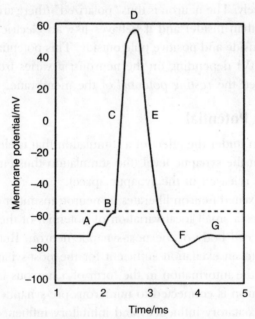

Fig. 2.2 The action potential: A. The neuron is polarized; B. The critical threshold of depolarization is reached and the sodic canals open; C. Massive entry of Na+ ions and strong depolarization takes place; D. Closing of sodic canals and opening of potassic canals occurs; E. Exit of K+ ions and repolarization of the membrane occurs; F. The neuron is hyperpolarized and refracted on new stimulation; G. The neuron is again at its resting potential and the "sodium–potassium" pump causes the exit of Na+ ions and entry of K+ ions.

The rise and propagation of action potential are the result of movements of ions between the exterior and interior of the membrane resulting from the opening of ionic canals sensitive to voltage that are thus closed when the neuron is at rest. The potential passage of the membrane to -40 mV is accompanied by an opening of ionic canals specific to sodium, which is manifested in an entry of Na+ ions to the interior of the membrane and has the effect of depolarizing the neuron (the membrane potential is less negative). This phenomenon has the consequence of the opening of new Na+ canals, activated by voltage, and the increasingly massive entry of Na+ ions. Then, the strong depolarization of neuron that results and reaches about +35 mV leads to the closing of Na+ canals and simultaneously the opening of canals specific to potassium activated by voltage; the K+ ions begin to leave the membrane, which has the effect of repolarizing the neuron. But at this stage, the concentrations of sodium and potassium ions from one side and the other of the membrane are not the resting concentrations. To reach that, it is necessary to make the K+ ions return to the interior and get the Na+ ions out, which is ensured by the sodium–potassium pump. Finally, the neuron passes through a short phase of hyperpolarization where the membrane potential is less than -70 mV (this is the refractory period of the neuron) before its potential can return to the normal resting value (-70 mV).

2.2.4 Propagation of Action Potential: Role of the Myelin Sheath

A particular glial cell has been mentioned earlier: the Schwann cell, which surrounds the neurons and forms the myelin sheath. The myelin sheath increases the diameter of the axon and is interrupted at regular intervals. The points of interruption are called *nodes of Ranvier* and they correspond to the places at which the axon is not covered by the myelin sheath. Because of this, the action potential is not propagated close together along the axon but only from one node of Ranvier to the next by "leaps": this is the saltatory conduction of action potential. The opening of ionic canals depending on the voltage occurs only at those places. This considerably accelerates the transmission of action potential, and thus of information.

2.2.5 Synaptic Transmission

The arrival of action potential at the tip of the axon will cause a set of chemical reactions. In the ends called "terminal buttons" of the axon, chemical molecules (designated "precursors" of neurotransmitters) stored in the synaptic vesicles transform, by means of the intervention of an enzyme, into neurotransmitters that accumulate in the terminal buttons. When the action potential reaches this end, it causes the opening of the specific canals of calcium (depending on voltage), which has the effect of penetrating the Ca++ ions present in the extracellular medium within the cell, which causes the liberation of neurotransmitters by the synaptic vesicles, in the synaptic pore. The neurotransmitter thus released fixes on its post-synaptic receptors, which has the effect of opening the specific ionic canals (of certain ions) that differ according to the neurotransmitter. Thus, according to the canals that open, it will be one ion or another that penetrates, which manifests itself in a de- or hyperpolarization. It is in this sense that a neurotransmitter can be exciter (causing a depolarization) or inhibitor (causing a hyperpolarization). In case of polarization, the cycle restarts from the beginning of what has been described on the genesis of action potential. After that, the neurotransmitter that has been liberated and fixed on its post-synaptic receptor desolidarizes from it, returns to the synaptic space, and is recaptured by the pre-synaptic neuron.

2.2.6 Coding of Information by the Action Potential

We have earlier said that the action potential does not vary in amplitude. Therefore, the question that is posed is: how does the intensity of stimulation manifest itself? The basic principle of this coding is the frequency of the action potential: the more the intensity of the stimulation increases, the more the frequency of the action potential increases. In fact, there are several types of neurons: some discharge only at the beginning of the stimulation (these are called phasic neurons), and others discharge all along the stimulation (tonic neurons), and still others called phasico-tonic have a burst of activity at the beginning and end of the stimulation but also have a tonic activity. Thus, the nervous system is informed by the beginning, intensity, and end of the stimulation.

To conclude, the nervous influx circulates from the axon of the pre-synaptic neuron to the dendrites and cell body of the post-synaptic neuron. The information transmitted by the neuron is an electrical phenomenon along the axon and chemical at the synapse. The action potential results in a depolarization of the neuron at its soma but takes birth at the beginning of the axon.

2.3 MACROSCOPIC ORGANIZATION: ANATOMICAL AND FUNCTIONAL SUBDIVISIONS OF THE NERVOUS SYSTEM

The first major subdivision of the nervous system involves the central nervous system, which encompasses the brain proper, the cerebral trunk, and the spinal cord, and the peripheral nervous system, which is composed of three subsystems: the cranial nerves, the rachidian nerves, and the automatic nervous system.

2.3.1 The Central Nervous System (CNS)

For easier reference, a set of anatomical plates (Fig. 2.3) have been grouped at the end of this chapter.

The subdivisions of the CNS can be more or less fine depending on the level at which they are located (and on the animal species). This is why different names may be used depending on whether one looks with an anatomical perspective (microscopic structure of the region concerned), a functional perspective, or a developmental perspective. Moreover, the denomination of cerebral areas is not the same in animals and humans. Finally, anatomists are not always unanimous on the place of a particular structure in one or another part of the brain.

First, the CNS has seven fundamental parts: the spinal cord, the bulb (or myelencephalus, a term used by developmental specialists), the pons, the cerebellum (which constitutes the metencephalus), the middle brain (mesencephalus), the diencephalus (thalamus and hypothalamus), and the cerebral hemispheres (or telencephalus).[3]

The brain proper is made up of cerebral hemispheres and the diencephalus but, by extension, the term *brain* is often used to signify the encephalus: anterior brain, middle brain, and posterior brain.[4]

The term *cerebral trunk* includes the posterior brain and the middle brain. Note that certain anatomists place the diencephalus in the cerebral trunk. The posterior brain includes the cerebellum, the reticulated formation, the pons, and the bulb. The tectum—with its superior colliculus and inferior colliculus—and the tegmentum—with its numerous nuclei, including black matter—constitute the middle brain.

Finally, the three principal structures of the anterior brain are the cortex, the limbic system and the basal ganglia.

---

[3] In a complementary manner, developmentalists still talk of the "prosencephalus" with respect to the anterior brain, of the "rhombencephalus" with respect to the posterior brain.

[4] Other terms are still used: rostral (anterior or towards the nose, the front), caudal (posterior or towards the feet, the tail), dorsal, ventral, lateral (towards the outside), medial (towards the middle line).

(a) The cerebral hemispheres

In humans, the cerebral hemispheres are so voluminous (85% of the weight of the total brain) that they conceal the other parts of the brain, except the cerebellum, the bulb and the pons, which are visible in lateral view.

The surface of cerebral hemispheres, or cortex (which means bark), is greatly wrinkled and thus presents convolutions or gyri and grooves or sulci, the largest of which are fissures.[5] Around 1.5 to 4.5 mm thick depending on the regions, the cortex is made up of several layers of cells (the number of layers depends on the region): it contains the somas, dendrites and part of the axons of neurons of these layers, the axons and terminations of neurons coming from other regions, and blood vessels. There are nevertheless the somas of neurons that predominate, which give to the cortex a grey colour, whence the name grey matter. It is important to understand well that the cortex occupies the gyri and the space located within the grooves and fissures. In humans, the surface of the cortex (stated as 1.6 to 2.5 m^2 depending on the author) is thus much greater than that of the skull, which is much less so in the case of other mammals. The cortex constitutes 80% of the anterior brain volume. Thus, the quantity of grey matter contained in the human cortex is, proportionately, greater or much greater in humans than in rats, cats or even the big apes.

In reality, the envelope of the brain is made up of the cortex—an envelope that appeared in the most recent species in the evolutionary scale— and the paleocortex, an envelope of more primitive species such as birds and reptiles. In humans, the paleocortex appears only in some regions that are not covered by the neocortex, that is, certain structures of the limbic system. The neocortex includes six layers of cells (numbered in Roman numerals), while the paleocortex contains only three or four. These layers of cells take on particular importance. In fact, they are made up of cells that differ in number and in form depending on the layer. Moreover, within a single layer, the architecture of cells differs from one region to the other. By means of these specific characteristics, the cortex communicates with most of the other parts of the brain and, at the same time, each area of the cortex makes use of its own network of connections adapted to its function. For example, layer 14, which receives afferent information, is denser and thicker in the sensory regions while it is the layer V, from which efferent information is sent, that is denser and thicker in the motor areas.

---

[5] As we go higher up the evolutionary ladder, this surface becomes more pleated and the cortex presents more gyri and sulci.

Grooves that are deeper than others—fissures—divide each of the cerebral hemispheres[6] into four major parts or lobes. The lateral fissure or Sylvian fissure separates the frontal lobe from the temporal lobe. The central grove or fissure, or the Rolando fissure, separates the frontal lobe from the parietal lobe. The parieto-occipital fissure separates the parietal lobe from the occipital lobe. The interhemispheric fissure separates the right and left cerebral hemispheres. These are nevertheless connected with each other by the callous bodies and the anterior commissure, a large bundle of myelinized nerve fibres that link each region of one hemisphere to the equivalent region of the other hemisphere.

If the lobes are anatomically and functionally different regions, much finer subdivisions better reflect the functional architecture of the cortex. From 1909, Brodmann, on the basis of the morphology and organization of cells of each region studied, identified some 50 cortical areas. His classification is still current today, although (1) some anatomists have ultimately listed a larger number of areas, (2) an evolution of this classification can be expected with technological advances, and finally (3) the numeration of Brodmann, resulting from the order in which he identified the areas, is hardly practical. Some regions of the cortex are finely divided into clearly identified, distinct functional units—the different visual areas of the occipital cortex, for example—while other regions, such as the prefrontal cortex, are much less finely divided.

Generally, it is possible to associate the principal functions of each lobe. For example, the occipital lobe contains areas of visual treatment, the parietal lobe contains somaesthetic areas, the tempo. al lobe contains areas of auditory treatment, and the frontal lobe contains motor areas. But these are certainly not the only functions of these lobes. To cite only this example, the frontal lobe, beyond its motor functions, is characterized by its primary role in executive functions. The frontal lobe may be composed in three parts, the prefrontal part of which is the most important in humans (more than half of the frontal lobe in humans but much less in other species). This prefrontal cortex receives afferences from nearly the entire parietal cortex and the temporal cortex, certain structures of the occipital cortex, but also very many sub-cortical structures (thalamus, basal ganglia, cerebellum, hippocampus, amygdala, cerebral trunk), which could allow us to understand its essential role in the coordination of multiple treatments operated in numerous regions of the CNS.

---

[6] Since there are two cerebral hemispheres, all the structures found in the brain are in twos, one for each hemisphere: two central fissures, two frontal lobes, etc.

Moreover, several classifications of different cortical areas can be made. Primary areas of the unimodal associative areas—associating information from one sensory modality—must be distinguished from multimodal associative areas, associating information issuing from various sensory modalities. To illustrate this, we may use the metaphor of Proust's "madeleine". As far as visual stimulus, the information from the retina, translated into electromagnetic waves emitted by different luminous "points" of the madeleine and its environment, comes after relay into the thalamus, to the primary visual areas of the occipital cortex (areas 17, now called areas V1,[7] or striated visual cortex). Then, this information is integrated into unimodal associative areas of vision (the extra-striate visual cortex), which makes it possible to identify a madeleine. Finally, the information is thus transmitted into multimodal associative areas and it is by means of the treatments realized in these that we may have the impression of "sensing the odour and taste of the madeleine", simply on seeing it. Note that, although the unimodal associative areas are located near the primary areas, the multimodal associative areas are more or less distant.

If various multimodal associative regions can be identified, it is important to recall that the frontal lobe, more precisely the prefrontal cortex, constitutes a gigantic place of association, the importance of which, in humans, has nothing in common with that observed in other mammals, which is attributed to the area that it occupies or to its role in the control of what is today summarized generally as "executive functions" (planning of action, memory of work).

(b) Basal ganglia

Also called central grey nuclei (CGN), the basal ganglia are three large subcortical nuclei, buried in the depths of the hemispheres. The caudate nucleus, the putamen, and the globus pallidus. These are thus clusters of neurons—or rather their somas—that receive afferences of the cortex and are implicated in complex motor functions. Very similar in structural and functional plan, the caudate nucleus and the putamen constitute the striatum.[8] Some neuroanatomists also include in the CGN the subthalamic nuclei and, above all, black matter. Beyond this debate between anatomists, we retain that with motor and pre-motor areas of the cortex and the thalamus,

---

[7] These different appellations correspond to nomenclatures established by different methods: anatomical or physiological.

[8] Some rather use the term *neostriatum* with respect to these two nuclei and *paleostriatum* with respect to the globus pallidus.

the CGN, the subthalamic nucleus and black matter are implicated in the circuits of motor control. For example, Parkinson's syndrome—with notably its trembling, its muscular rigidity—is associated with dysfunction of the nigro-striate dopaminergic pathway (i.e., between black matter and the striatum).

(c) *The limbic system*

The limbic system is located in the periphery (this is the meaning of the word *limbic*) of the telencephalus and the diencephalus. It was McLean who, in 1952, with his "theory of three brains",[9] popularized the term *limbic system* (Broca had introduced the term *large limbic lobe*) and associated it with the circuit of emotion. In fact, this circuit was described by Papez in the 1930s.

The limbic system is a network of structures that do not constitute an anatomical entity. On the one hand, some of its structures belong to the telencephalus, and others to the diencephalus. On the other hand, it also includes subcortical cerebral nuclei as well as bandlets of cortex (more precisely of palaeocortex). The hippocampus, also called the cornu ammonis, is an ancient cortical structure (in the scale of evolution) located in the internal part of the temporal lobe, the form of which resembles the fish of the same name. Near the hippocampus is the para-hippocampic gyrus. Above the callous bodies, the cingular gyrus extends from the front to the rear. The amygdala is a small nucleus in the form of a bulb, located in the depths of the anterior part of the temporal lobe, which anatomists class among the central grey nuclei, but that they distinguish from the latter by its numerous relationships with different sensory areas and with the hypothalamus and by its role in the emotions. In this network, we can also cite other structures: the septum, the fornix cerebri, but also the olfactory bulb (not very important in humans) and structures that belong to the diencephalus, that is, the mamillary bodies and the hypothalamus. If the knowledge of the detailed functioning of this system is in constant evolution, it is known at least that many signals that issue from it are sent towards the hypothalamus and towards the cerebral trunk, playing an essential role in the control of human behaviours. Its role in the formation of memory—to which we will return—may also be noted.

(d) *The diencephalus*

The diencephalus is made up of the thalamus and the hypothalamus, two structures located one above the other.

---

[9] This theory postulates that "three" layers of the brain are developed by "piling up" in the course of evolution: the reptilian brain (or cerebral trunk), paleo-mammalian brain (or limbic system) and the neo-mammalian brain (or neo-cortex).

Located in front of the cerebral trunk, the thalamus is a bilateral structure made up of a set of nuclei. It is first of all a gigantic relay on all the sensory pathways, with the exception of certain pathways of olfaction. From these relays, the information is transported towards the primary visual cortex via the lateral geniculate body of the thalamus, while information from the internal ear is transported towards the primary auditory cortex via the medial geniculate body. The thalamus also plays a role in integration (interpretation) of information. This role is less important in humans than in other species but allows the thalamus to participate in coding of sensitivity to pain and its intensity. It is also in bidirectional relation (by afferences and efferences) with different structures of motor circuits (CGN, cerebellum, cortex), by which it participates in muscular control. Finally, we must mention the role of one of its most important nuclei in attentional control: this is the pulvinar, interconnected with other regions implicated in the circuits of attention, particularly the posterior parietal cortex.

The hypothalamus is located just below the thalamus. Composed of 22 small nuclei, representing hardly 0.3% of the volume of the brain, it plays an essential role in the maintenance of homeostasy [the regulation of most behaviours, particularly the basic behaviours that ensure survival of the individual or species (e.g., hunger, thirst, thermoregulation, sleep, hormonal function, sexual behaviour)]. This role is impossible to dissociate on the one hand from the hypophysis, the small endocrine gland located under the hypothalamus, by which the hypothalamus controls the endocrine system of hormonal secretions carried by the blood, and on the other hand from the automatic nervous system (ANS, to which we will return later) that the hypothalamus controls. But the role of the hypothalamus cannot be understood unless one knows that it receives afferences of the limbic system, amygdala, retina (which informs it about light-dark alternation), and the reticulate formation of the cerebral trunk, while in turn it projects on the prefrontal cortex, the spinal cord, the amygdala. Note that the hypothalamus is made up of two major types of cells: nerve cells proper, starting point for the neuronal pathway by which the hypothalamus triggers rapid reactions via the ANS, and neuro-secretory cells, starting point of the humoral pathway, by which the hypothalamus directly or indirectly controls the secretion of numerous hormones. The plant modifications, apart from emotional reactions, result from the putting into play—varying according to factors such as type of reaction, the internal state of the individual—of these two types of pathways. The reactions of stress agents rely primarily on the neuronal pathway for a rapid adaptation of the organisms and then on the humoral pathway for a more long-term adaptation.

(e) *The cerebral trunk*

The cerebral trunk constitutes the intermediary level between the spinal cord and the brain is partly hidden, at the rear, by the cerebellum, which covers it. It thus comprehends the rachidian bulb[10] (or myelencephalus) in its more caudal part, just above the spinal cord, then the mesencephalus and finally the metencephalus (or pons). It is a complex region.

It is primarily a "passageway" of ascending and descending fibres through which information is transported in both directions between the periphery (the spinal cord), the brain and the cerebellum. Coming from the spinal cord, the sensory fibres relay in the higher and lower colliculi[11] of the mesencephalus and are thus transported towards the thalamus, then from there to the cortex. Coming from the cortex, the descending fibres, after passage in the cerebral trunk, are then transported towards the medulla and the cerebellum. It is at the cerebral trunk that there is decussation of ascending and descending fibres by which each side of the body projects or is commanded by the controlateral cerebral hemisphere.

The cerebral trunk, by its own neurons and nuclei, is also the site of entry and exit of sensory and motor fibres of the face, mouth, respiratory system and heart, which do not transit through the spinal cord.

The reticulated formation constitutes a very important structure that extends all along the cerebral trunk: a vast network of fibres and neurons receiving information from various origins, it contributes to the maintenance of vigilance (a lesion of the reticulated formation is manifested by a state similar to sleep).

Finally, it can be underlined that a lesion of the cerebral trunk has consequences that are often more serious than a lesion of the brain proper, taking into account on the one hand the role of this structure in functions as vital as vigilance, respiration or cardiac function, and on the other hand its small size. In humans, severance of the cerebral trunk leads to death.

(f) *The cerebellum*

The cerebellum is the structure that covers the cerebral trunk and is connected at the pons. Like the telencephalus, it comprises, on each side, two hemispheres that, unlike the cerebral hemispheres, control the part of the body that is ipsilateral to them. The medial part of the cerebellum is the vermis, a non-lateralized structure that separates the two cerebellum hemispheres and that

---

[10] Often called *bulb*, not to be confused with the olfactory bulb, which is located in the telencephalus.

[11] The colliculi are also called, now rarely, *quadruplet tubercles*.

controls axial motoricity. Like the cerebral hemispheres, the cerebellum is covered by a cortex that is greatly furrowed. It has three cell layers: the middle layer is composed of Purkinje cells, large multipolar neurons with highly complex dendritic organization, fan-shaped, which projects on the molecular layer (exterior) and makes a synapse with the deep neurons of the cerebellum; those neurons are the origin of projections of the cerebellum on other nervous structures, notably toward the descending motor pathways that are directed toward the spinal cord, but also the thalamus and the motor and premotor cortices. It is important to note that the neurotransmitter of Purkinje cells, the GABA, is an inhibitor, which gives them an inhibitory role. Thus, the cerebellum plays an essential role in posture, walking, and coordination of movements: because of the cerebellum, movements are smooth and not abrupt.

(g) *The spinal cord*

The spinal cord is the lowest part of the CNS (in the erect body of humans). It is also the last part of the CNS before the peripheral nervous system. Protected by vertebrae of the spine, which it crosses longitudinally, it transports sensory information from the periphery to the brain and motor information from the brain to the periphery. It is through the spinal cord that motor orders are directed toward the muscles and sensory messages informing the brain about the skin, state of muscles, tendons and joints. It also comprises bundles—ascending and descending—of fibres transporting this information, constituted of myelinized axons (this is the white matter of the spinal cord). It also comprises, in the central part of the grey matter made up of cell bodies of sensory neurons, motoneurons and small interneurons. When a cross-section is made on the spinal cord, this grey matter is clearly visible—in a butterfly shape—surrounding the white matter. Motor commands going from the spinal cord towards the periphery leave the spinal cord by ventral roots of the anterior part, while sensory information penetrates the spinal cord by dorsal roots of its posterior part. The spinal cord is thus a virtual interface between the CNS and the peripheral nervous system. But it is also the site of reflex activities.[12]

(h) *Protection and vascularization of CNS*

The brain and spinal cord are not protected by the cranial os and the vertebrae alone. In fact, they are enveloped in three membranes, the meninges. The outermost is the dura mater. The innermost is the pia mater, a fine

---

[12] For example, the patellar reflex by which a tap on the knee leads in a relaxed person to a slight movement of the leg.

membrane firmly adhering to the brain and covered by numerous blood vessels. Between these two vessels, the arachnoid[13] is the most delicate. The space between the pia mater and the arachnoid is full of cerebrospinal fluid (CSF), a clear and transparent liquid that nourishes the brain and absorbs shocks and that "bathes" the brain and spine. Because of the CSF, a shock or acceleration of the head does not lead to movement of the brain within the skull.

Like all cells, the neurons need a large amount of energy to function (fuel in the form of glucose and oxygen to achieve the combustions needed to transform the fuel into energy). The brain, however, has no reserves of oxygen and glucose. Thus, there must be a constant inflow of oxygen and glucose. This is possible because of an extremely dense network of blood vessels branching from small arteries, which themselves branch from large arteries. The vertebral arteries and the carotid arteries are the two major basic pathways that are subdivided into smaller arteries distributed in the different regions of the brain, which are divided in turn into blood vessels that cover the pia mater before penetrating and embedding themselves in the subjacent brain. The distribution of nutrients to neurons of different parts of the brain as well as the elimination of wastes occur through blood capillaries, the walls of which are much more watertight than that of capillaries in the rest of the body. Thus, the capillaries of the CNS allow water and nutrients (glucose, amino acids) to flow, but filter large molecules (wastes, proteins, and toxins) susceptible of damaging the nervous tissue.[14] This mechanism, which ensures the protection of the CNS, is called the *blood-brain barrier.*

2.3.2 The Peripheral Nervous System (PNS)

The peripheral nervous system is located outside the osseous parts (skull and spinal column) that protect the CNS. It comprises the somatic nervous system and the visceral or automatic nervous system (ANS).

(a) *The somatic nervous system*

The nerves that make up the somatic nervous system transmit information from the CNS (brain or spinal cord) to the periphery (muscles) by motor pathways and from the periphery to the CNS by sensory pathways.

---

[13] From the Greek *arachne* or spider. The arachnoid has the appearance of a spider web.

[14] The filtering applies also to certain drug molecules, which poses a problem in treating certain infections.

Cranial nerves

Twelve pairs of cranial nerves (listed by roman numerals: I, II, XII) relate the different parts of the head (eye, ear, language, face) to the brain and cross the cranium through small orifices. Some of these nerves are strictly sensory, others are strictly motor, and still others are mixed. One of them (the vagus nerve X that emerges from the rachidian bulb) extends beyond the head toward the viscera and belongs also to the ANS.

Rachidian nerves

The rachis (or spinal column) is made up of a chain of 33 vertebrae distributed in three sections: cervical (from C1 to C7), dorsal (or thoracic, T1 to T12), lumbar (L1 to L5), sacral and coccygeal. These vertebrae, hollow in the centre—allowing the passage of the spinal cord—also have small orifices on the side, crossed by rachidian nerves, which ensure the transport of sensory and motor information between the periphery and the CNS (spinal cord). These rachidian or spinal nerves (there are 31 pairs of nerves with a nerve for each side) are named for the vertebrae they cross (first cervical nerve). Thus, the cervical rachidian nerves innervate the nape of the neck, the thoracid nerves innervate the thorax and upper limbs, and the lumbar and sacral nerves innervate the lower back and lower limbs.

Each rachidian nerve thus comprises two branches, joined in a peripheral nerve up to the spinal ganglion, but separated into roots near the spinal cord within the vertebral column. Thus, the ventral root can be distinguished by whether what is transported is the efferent motor information from the dorsal root or the sensory afferent information. At the spinal cord, these nerves come into contact with descending and ascending bundles that cover the medulla and towards the brain.

(b) *The automatic nervous system (ANS)*

The automatic nervous system ensures the regulation, largely automatic, involuntary and unconscious, of the activity of the viscera, glands and vascularization. The functioning of the ANS is regulated, essentially, by the hypothalamus.

From the brain and spinal cord, "autonomous" neurons come to innervate other neurons, the cell bodies of which are located in the ganglia, and that will innervate the principal organs of the human body.

The ANS comprises two systems:

1. The sympathetic system, the ganglia of which are arranged along the spinal column (on each side) at the thoracic and lumbar regions, and that communicates with the spinal nerves and the internal organs of the body.
2. The parasympathetic system, the ganglia of which are dispersed throughout the body near the organs that they innervate and that innervate the organs through the vagus.

A number of organs are innervated by the two systems that act in an opposing manner (for example, the sympathetic system accelerates the cardiac rhythm, while the parasympathetic system slows it down). Generally, the two systems complement each other. The sympathetic system is active in short-term responses of the body (running, fleeing), while the parasympathetic system is implicated in long-term reactions (regulation of energy reserves, immune defences).

Figure 2.3 shows the various parts of the brain.

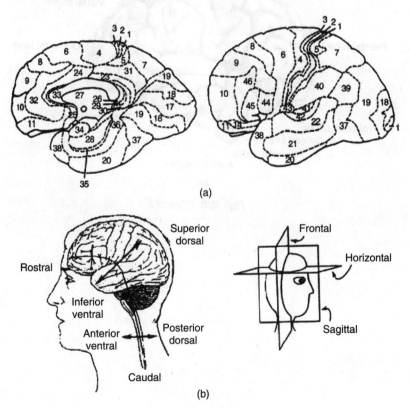

(a)

(b)

Fig. 2.3 *(Contd.)*

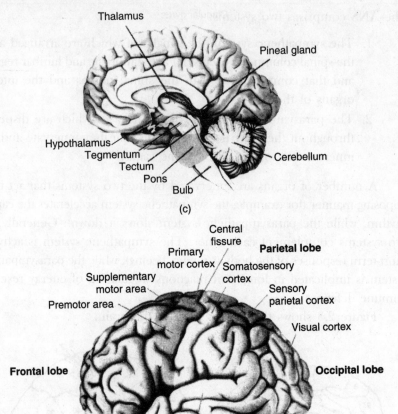

(c)

(d)

Fig. 2.3 *(Contd.)*

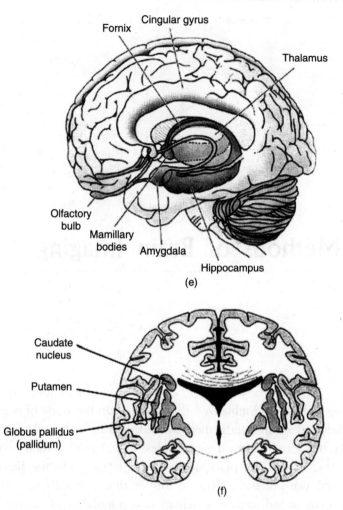

Fig. 2.3 The brain: (a) Brodmann areas (left, medial view; right, lateral view); (b) Appellations (left) and cross-sections (right); (c) Sagittal section of the brain, cerebellum and cerebral trunk; (d) Lobes, principal fissures and areas (note that the insula is not visible: it is located below the Sylvian fissure); (e) Limbic system; (f) Central grey nuclei (frontal section of brain).

3

Methods of Brain Imaging

Over the past 20 years, the advent and development of functional methods of brain imaging have undoubtedly led to progress in the study of cognitive functions. Before describing these methods and showing in them the potential uses for psychologists, we must nevertheless "clear out" certain received ideas or myths. In the first place, one does not "see" into the brain, no more than one can see the activity of this or that neuron: one can only visualize—directly or indirectly—the activity of a population of neurons in a more or less precise region of the brain. Moreover, to visualize the cerebral activity serves no purpose if one knows nothing of the cognitive functions involved. In other words, these methods have no utility if they are applied without hypotheses about the models of cognitive functioning, elaborated notably by psychologists, and if the experimental paradigms have not been conceived to test such models. The methods of brain imaging thus can not replace theoretical reflection or experimental procedure. The data that result from it thus complement conventionally acquired behavioural data in cognitive psychology.

That said, in a process of study of cognitive functions the relationship between behaviour and cerebral function is effectively relevant. This is what was done by the "fathers" of neuropsychology when they compared the clinical profile and post-mortem examination of the brains of their patients (such as Broca in the study of his patient Tan-Tan; see Chapter 6). The methods of brain imaging are about to enrich this procedure and, most of all, they avoid, at least partly, the classic pitfalls of neuropsychology, such as localizing the deficient cognitive function in the injured region when this is integrated in a set of neuronal networks and when the deficiencies originate from the interruption of these networks because of the focal lesion.

The active brain is one in which populations of neurons are active—an activity that is of course much more than the simple basic discharge of neurons. The methods of brain imaging are all designed to measure—directly or indirectly—this activity of neuron populations.

It is known that active neurons generate electric currents (action potentials propagated by axons, post-synaptic potentials that, depending on the case, can be exciters or inhibitors). The synaptic electrical currents generate variants of magnetic field. The variations of these post-synaptic electric currents and magnetic fields are basically *direct methods* of brain imaging (electro-encephalography or EEG and magneto-encephalography or MEG). But an active neuron consumes energy and oxygen; it thus requires a local increase in blood flow. The methods of brain imaging based on these metabolic changes constitute the second major category of methods. This is functional magnetic resonance imaging (fMRI) and positron emission tomography (PET). These are called *indirect methods* because the extent of these metabolic changes is only an indirect measure of the electrical activity of neurons.

3.1 DIRECT METHODS: EEG AND MEG

The data from EEG and MEG directly reflect the neuronal activity, but it must be kept in mind that it is the activity—more precisely post-synaptic potentials (PSP)—of neuron populations (100,000 to 1 million) active at the same time (since the PSP lasts only a few tens of milliseconds) in a space of a few cubic millimetres of the cortex. In any case, EEG and MEG are not measures of action potential of a neuron (which lasts no more than a few milliseconds). The spaces in which these synchronous activities of neurons are emitted are called *functional macrocolumns* that behave like dipoles of current whose direction corresponds to the average direction of the neurons involved. The response recorded in EEG is parallel to the direction of the dipole while the response recorded in MEG is perpendicular to it. These methods record the signal that has crossed the scalp, emanating from a large number of neurons.

3.1.1 EEG

Except in the case of highly specific intracranial recording (for example, in epileptic patients in which electrodes have been implanted, for therapeutic purposes, directly in certain parts of the brain), EEG activity is recorded using signal-receiving electrodes placed on the surface of the scalp. The activity thus collected results from the sum of PSP corresponding to the implementation synchronous with a multitude of neurons oriented in the same direction, a condition necessary for the summation of PSP. Taking into account different cerebral protections, the signal recorded is greatly attenuated (a few microvolts). It thus must be amplified to be detectable. At present, there are four helmets, provided with 32, 64, or 128 electrodes, which must be placed on the head of the subject under rigorous controls. In fact, the placement of these electrodes must correspond to the same cerebral regions in all subjects, no matter what the size of their heads. When the technical means of arrangement allow it, it is preferable to arrange brain images of each subject (collected by atomic magnetic resonance imaging), which makes it possible to locate precisely each of these electrodes for each subject with respect to the position of grooves and gyri, because this varies from one individual to another. Of course, when the helmet contains more electrodes, the spatial precision of regions explored is greater, but also the ultimate treatments on the signals recorded will be longer.

The signal thus recorded is presented in the form of a succession of short waves, the spontaneous or "rough" EEG, which differ in sequence (in hertz) and amplitude (in microvolts)—of rhythms alpha, beta, theta, etc.—that can be related with levels of sleep and waking. This rough EEG is often charged with artefacts of various origins: muscular activity (e.g., a subject with clenched teeth), ocular activity (blinking eyes), cardiac rhythm (the electrode is placed on a small arteriole), electrodermal activity (the skin sweats), or very simply a movement of current from an electrode. These artefacts may greatly disturb the EEG signal and must thus be eliminated as far as possible, either at the source (for example, one asks the subject to relax or not blink) or after the fact—there are software programs that make it possible to "correct" to some extent the EEG signal distorted by ocular movements.

But it is important to know that, at present, it is not this "rough" signal resulting from the analysis of waves of the gamma band, whose frequency is around 40 Hz, that is significant with respect to cognitive activities.

3.1.2 MEG

The MEG technique records, near the scalp, the cerebral magnetic fields produced by the same synaptic currents as those that are recorded by EEG. This is a much more recent technique than EEG, but requires much more complicated equipment; studies that use it are increasingly numerous but still limited. The equipment comprises magnetic field detectors, made up of a bobbin of conducting metal wire (magnetometers). These are in a supraconductor environment, without resistance, that allows the fields generated—which are very weak—to be detected. This supraconductor environment is possible only if the magnetometers are plunged in liquid helium cooled to -270°C. This is the reason the equipment includes a large tube (around a metre long for a diameter of around 50 cm) located above the head of the subject in which the detectors are coupled with SQUID (supraconducting quantum interference device) to ensure their cooling. The equipment thus comprises a certain number of captors—100 to 300—fixed by the manufacturer; it is not the experimenter who fixes the number, as he or she can for the EEG, and its captors are thus a few centimetres from the scalp of the subject.

3.1.3 Evoked Potentials (EPs)[1]

When a subject perceives stimuli (of any nature) and/or when the subject is engaged in a cognitive task, the perception of stimulus and the cognitive treatments that follow generate potentials of very low amplitude (a few microvolts) that are not visible on the track of the rough EEG (the amplitude of which is several tens of microvolts), reproducible from one assay to another. These are EPs linked to the event[2] (by the stimuli or by the cognitive treatments implicated in the task). Because of the reproducible character of these potentials (such EP occurs always in the same region and in the same range of post-stimulus latency for a single situation), it is possible to visualize them, and thus subsequently to measure them, using the technique of averages.

The principle of averages is the following: the EEG is continuously recorded (on the computer) while the subject is given a succession of stimuli, which could be different, calling for one or more responses. Using an adapted software program, portions of the EEG are then grouped (on a

---

[1] Because of the still limited number of data on magnetic evoked fields, this section is limited to electric evoked potentials.

[2] ERPs: evoked related potentials.

time window chosen beforehand, e.g., 200 ms before to 1000 ms after the stimulus) according to identical situations (same stimulus and same response) and the signal recorded on each electrode in the temporal window is added, for each type of situation. Let us take, for example, a subject placed in a situation in which one must deliver to it randomly two stimuli S1 and S2 to which it is necessary to bring, respectively, responses R1 and R2. Thus there is a series of "pairs" S1R1, S1R1, S2R2, S1R1, S2R2, S2R2, S1R1, S2R2, etc. The data processing program groups and adds, for each of the electrodes, all the "portions" of the EEG signal corresponding to, on the one hand, S1R1 pairs and on the other hand the S2R2 pairs, this in a temporal window of x ms fixed by the experimenter (y ms before S and z ms after S, R having been delivered in the interval).

To the extent that the average carries on a sufficient number of assays (at least 50 to 60 identical assays[3]), the rough EEG signal summed over the entire set of identical assays will be annulled—it thus corresponds to a background noise—while the EP, identical to an assay of the other, will be amplified by this summation (see Fig. 3.1). On each electrode, therefore, we observe a succession of waves (negative and positive) marking the stages of the treatment of information consecutive to the deliverance of stimulus and, if need be, to the programming of the response.

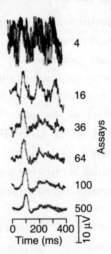

Fig. 3.1 Averaging (Dawson, 1951). From top to bottom: EEG is averaged over 4, 16, 36, 64, 100, and 500 assays. If the number of assays averaged is high, the evoked potential emerges from the background noise to that extent.

---

[3] That is, for the preceding example, 50 to 60 S1R1 assays and 50 to 60 S2R2 assays.

This succession of waves differs according to the type of treatment operated. It is generally represented in the form of chronograms (one chronogram per electrode) in which time figures on the abscissa and where amplitude of the wave, on the ordinate axis, is conventionally directed towards the top for negative waves and towards the bottom for positive waves.[4] When the EEG has been recorded on a large number of electrodes (at least 32), one can also, subject to the availability of mapping software, visualize in the form of maps of potential the activity recorded on all the electrodes, at an instant t, on a sphere standing for the head of the subject.

3.1.4 The Different Waves of Evoked Potential

First, it must be clarified that *waves of evoked potential, evoked potential,* and *components of evoked potential* are equivalent terms used interchangeably in the literature.

The EPs are identifiable by their polarity (positive P, negative N), the latency of their peak (for example, N100 is a negative wave whose peak of amplitude lasts 100 ms post-stimulus), and their topography (i.e., the location on the scalp of this peak of amplitude).

There are several types of classification of EP. Here the discussion is limited to distinguishing the exogenous EP from endogenous EP. This is a useful classification, even though not faultless (there is a certain temporal overlapping between the two types; one can influence the other).

Exogenous EP, which occur earlier, survive for a delay of 150-200 ms post-stimulus (at the level of the cortex, the earliest are observable 50 ms post-stimulus). They are called *exogenous* because they mark the sensory treatments linked to stimulation. Observable on the electrodes placed near sensory areas where the afferent burst occurs (e.g., visual areas for a visual stimulus), their latency is identical from one assay to another (for a specific wave); on the other hand, their amplitude (or rather the amplitude of their peak) varies as a function of the physical characteristics of the stimulus. Their clinical use is important particularly when it must be ensured that the information contained in the stimulation effectively reaches the sensory cortex, but also that it plays a role in arousing the subject (in the case of N100, for example).

---

[4] Note that this convention tends to disappear. This is why it is important, when one reads a publication on the subject of EP, always to refer to the legend that indicates the way in which positive and negative waves are represented.

The endogenous EPs relate to the characteristics of the task, cognitive treatments that the subject effects to realize it, and the subject's attitude towards the task. Their latency is longer than that of exogenous EPs (generally more than 200 ms post-stimulus). It is obviously these that are most interesting to psychology and cognitive neuroscience. Several endogenous components have been identified and studied over time, since the advent of technologies of averaging. The list of waves of EP that follows is not exhaustive (see Fig. 3.2).

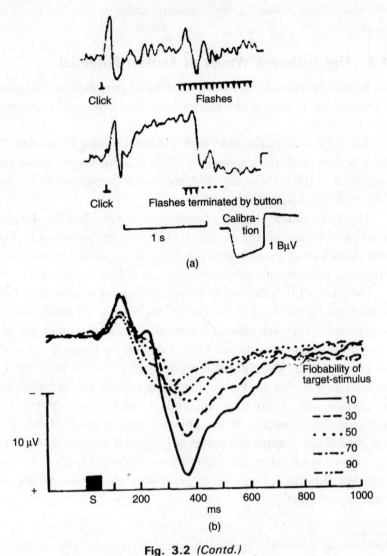

Fig. 3.2 (Contd.)

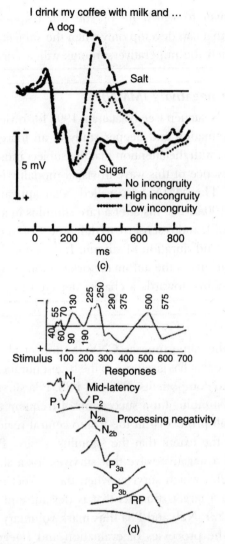

Fig. 3.2 Some evoked potential waves: (a) CVN; (b) P300; (c) N400; (d) Diagram of the temporal course of evoked potential: the peaks of different waves survive for different instants and allow TR fragmentation in intermediary delays.

Contingent negative variation (CNV)

Contingent negative variation was discovered in 1964 by Walter and his research team (Walter et al., 1964). This was a slow negative wave that develops in the fronto-central region between two stimuli associated in the particular context of the task: after a warning (or preparatory) stimulus, the subject waits for an imperative stimulus (which he or she knows will arrive) to which he or she will respond. It is thus an expected wave that can develop only when the subject can estimate the moment at which the imperative stimulus will occur.

The mismatch negativity (MMN)

The team of de Naatanen (see Naatanen, 1992 for review) is responsible for the implementation and deeper study of an increase in negativity of EP in relation with the attention that the subject must pay to auditory stimuli (the presence of this wave in visual modality is still not clearly demonstrated). The MMN (also called N2a) appears in the fronto-central region, 100 to 200 ms after a rare stimulus in a series of stimuli (oddball protocol[5]), and is sensitive to differences of frequency, intensity, spatial location, and duration of stimuli. Independent of the subject's consciousness, it marks the automatic orientation of attention towards the deviant stimulus, towards a change detected in the environment.

P300 (or P3)

Discovered at the same time as CNV (Sutton et al., 1965), P300 is probably the wave that has given rise to the largest number of publications. In fact, it has two components: P3a and P3b. P3a survives around 300 ms after a rare stimulus (in a succession of frequent and rare stimuli typical of oddball protocols) in the fronto-central region and it is thus more ample to the extent that the stimulus is rare. P3b forms often a complex with a negative wave that survives for a short time before it, N200 (or N2b), which survives when the subject must turn his or her attention to a target stimulus that is deviant and rare (Naatanen and Gaillard 1983). N2b and P3a thus mark voluntary orientation and correspond to the processes of evaluation and categorization of the stimulus.

---

[5] In an oddball protocol, the subject hears a succession of two sounds (one of high frequency, "bip", and the other of low frequency, "bop"), which appear at different intervals, e.g., 75% of high-frequency sounds (frequent stimuli) and 25% of low-frequency sounds (rare stimuli); thus, there is a sequence of the following type: bip, bip, bip, bop, bip, bip, bop, bip, bip, bip, bip, bop....

[6] An increasing number of publications distinguish P300 (P3b) from positive waves of long latency (we call them P600, for example). It is not yet known whether these positivities are late P300, generated by the same cerebral regions, or waves generated by other regions.

P3b survives later (300-800 ms post-stimulus[6]), in the parietal region. Its latency varies with the complexity of cognitive treatments carried out to achieve the task. An increasing number of publications distinguish P300 (P3b) from positive waves of long latency (such as P600). Whether these positivities are of slow P300 generated by the same cerebral regions, or waves generated by other regions, is not yet known. P3b marks the controlled processes of evaluation and categorization of significant stimuli in the context of the task. According to the authors, it is associated with various stages of treatment of information: identification of stimulus, choice of response, decision to act, and updating of the memory of the task.

N400

N400 was revealed by Kutas and Hillyard (1980) in the domain of language. It is a negativity that survives around 400 ms after the presentation of a "discordant" word with respect to the context of the phrase in which it was inserted (e.g., I drink my coffee with a dog). When this discordance is high, it has been described by its initial authors as a wave marking a semantic incongruity. Nevertheless, it has since been shown that it is also present for incongruities expressed in other stimuli: for example, if a subject is shown a photograph of a famous face with the region of the eyes masked (bait-stimulus that generates an expectation in the subject) and, just afterward (around 200 ms), shown the same face completed with the eyes of another person, an N400 appears bilaterally in the central region, while this is not the case if the face is completed by the eyes of the person presented in the fragment (see, e.g., Jemel et al., 1999). If there is a debate in the literature on the semantic character or otherwise of such an incongruity, here it is maintained that N400 appears when the fragment context an expectation of the subject and when there is an incongruity between what the subject expects and what is presented to him or her.

3.1.5 Advantages and Disadvantages of Evoked Potentials and Magnetic Fields

These two methods are non-invasive: they use no injected product or stimulation. They are thus totally inoffensive. EEG is a time-consuming technique, MEG is on the other hand very costly (for the equipment as well as the liquid helium bottles).

With respect to the location of active regions, EP and ME do not constitute an excellent method of imaging, even though the multiplication of number of electrodes in the last period has the effect of improving it. Maps of cerebral activities can be thus presented, but the basic problem is that an activity recorded on the surface of the scalp says nothing about the source of this activity. Although software is available for reconstruction or localization of sources of the EP and ME observed, their results are not certain. In fact, this is a matter of resolving what one calls the "inverse problem", to know how to infer the distribution of electrical currents within the brain from that measured on the surface (for EP) or at some centimetres from it (for the ME) and the resolution of this problem is not unambiguous.

Nevertheless, it is important to emphasize that the EEG and MEG are complementary methods and that, because of this, their combination improves the location of sources of signals received. In effect, because of the orthogonality of electrical currents and magnetic fields for a single dipole, the EEG detectors are more sensitive to deep sources than MEG detectors: for these deep sources, the EEG signal is thus strong while the MEG signal is weak. Moreover, the dipoles being entirely perpendicular to the surface of the cortex, they are perpendicular to the scalp on the gyri and parallel to the scalp in the grooves. Thus, the EEG records better than MEG the signals coming from the gyri than from the grooves and vice versa. The comparison of the amplitude of EEG and MEG signals for the same events thus suggests hypotheses on the location of sources: on the surface or in depths: on a gyrus or in a groove.

The EP and ME constitute excellent methods if one is interested in the temporal organization of steps of treatment of information. In fact, their temporal resolution is excellent—unequalled by any other method since it is of the order of milliseconds. Thus, in measuring the latences of EP and in studying their variations as a function of different modalities of experimental factors, one can precisely date the cognitive processes that generate waves. With the EP and ME, we have thus a virtual method of chronometry of mental operations since the waves identified constitute a sort of mark of processes that occur between the appearance of the stimulus and the subject's response (that is, reaction time, behavioural index, overall).

3.2 INDIRECT METHODS: PET AND fMRI

The methods of PET and fMRI, both founded on blood flow in the brain (thus metabolic methods), differ in their principle, in the variable measured, and in their applications.

3.2.1 PET

(a) *The principle*

The blood flow in a given part of the brain[7] is an indicator, a marker, of the metabolic activity of synapses of this region since the neurons in activity require an input of energy and oxygen carried by the blood, necessitating an increase of blood flow. The PET method allows the study, quantitative and local, of courses of molecules of blood in circulation in the brain, by means of radioactive marking of the oxygen contained in the water molecules present in the blood. To apply this technique, one must first inject in the blood, intravenously, a small quantity of water marked with radioactive oxygen. This radioactive water is distributed in the cerebral capillaries, in which it may partly pass thru the cerebral tissue (the remaining part distributed in the blood circulation). Normally, the nucleus of the oxygen (O^{16}) possesses 8 protons and 8 neutrons. But the nucleus of radioactive oxygen (O^{15}) has 8 protons and 7 neutrons: it is thus unstable and one of its protons is rapidly transformed into a neutron in emitting a positron. When a positron is emitted, it is combined immediately with an electron present in the ambient medium. This "particle-antiparticle" pair is annihilated, which leads to the liberation of two gamma photons that are emitted simultaneously in directions 180° opposite to each other (in a straight line). The blood flow increases and so does the probability of such an event (since a large quantity of unstable O^{15} is thus present). The gamma photons thus liberated are highly energetic and thus cross the brain and its various protective envelopes (cranium, skin) so well that they are detectable outside the cranium. Once they are outside the cranium, the photons can be detected if the head of the subject is placed in a positron camera.

The positron camera is a ring on which photon detectors are arranged all around the head of the subject. When two photons hit two detectors opposed with respect to the subject's head, there is detection of coincidence (see Fig. 3.3). The pair of detectors that are hit determines the side on which the photons are emitted resulting from the association of a positron to an electron. But to locate this precise point of the emission, several pairs must have been emitted in this point according to different lines, which is the case when the blood flow charged with radioactive oxygen increases.

---

[7] Here we discuss the use of PET in brain imaging, but PET is also used in medicine to study the functioning of various organs, notably in the case of suspicion of cancerous cells. The technique is thus slightly different in that it could use other markers such as $carbon_{11}$, $nitrogen_{13}$, and $fluorine_{18}$.

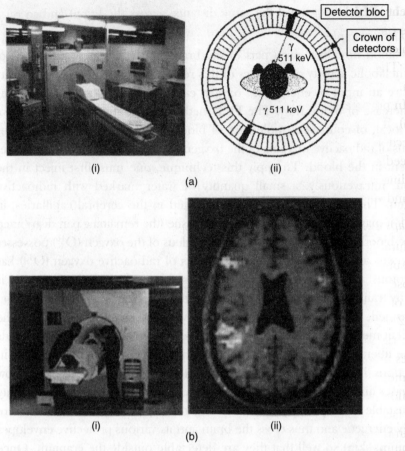

Fig. 3.3 PET (left) and MRI (right). Above, the apparatus in which the subject lies. Bottom left, the detector of coincidence of gamma photons of the PET: the head of the subject is located in the crown of detectors, which moves horizontally to realize "sections" of the brain; Bottom right, example of image obtained by MRI from a "section" of the brain.

The detection of several pairs of photons by the positron camera allows the tracing of several lines the intersection of which determines the region of emission of photons.

The subject is stretched out on a bed that is moved into the camera. Images of the brain are recorded in "sections" (Gk *tomos* signifies "section", hence the name tomography, section by section) as the bed moves forward, from which a map of the regional blood flow is thus obtained.

Of course, the data recorded by the detectors require sophisticated treatment by computer to correct accidental detections, the effect of attenuation to the extent that the photons come far from their point of emission (the different lines do not travel the same distance across the brain) and so on, before one can produce—or rather reconstruct—images of regions activated and integrate, as is often the case, these sections into the image of a complete brain. The spatial precision of the location of regions emitting photons is 8 mm.

In practice, because of its instability, O^{15} lasts for a short time (around 2 min). The radioactive water must thus be prepared immediately before its injection and the injection must be renewed during the experiment (hence the need to insert a catheter in a vein in the arm of the subject). The recording lasts 1 min 30 sec. An injection can be repeated only 8–10 min later and one cannot administer more than four injections.

(b) *Maps of differences: the subtractive method*

The duration of a recording being 90 sec, the use of PET during the time that a subject realizes cognitive tasks poses a thorny methodological problem. Suppose the subject is engaged in a task of face recognition in which a series of 30 photos are presented to him, at a rate of, for example, one every 2 sec, and in which the subject must respond by pressing the button on the right as soon as he recognizes the face, and the one on the left if he does not recognize it. Each "face-response" pair lasts around 1 sec. The experimental series lasts around 1 min, during which the variations in cerebral brain flow are recorded in order to localize the cerebral regions activated by the face recognition. During this minute of recording, the local variations of brain flow will be due to the task of recognition itself, as well as to visual perception (non-specific to face recognition), the programming of motor response, the cerebral activity corresponding to the activity of the subject during the inter-assay intervals, and other factors. It is necessary, thus, to define a control task during which there is recording of the cerebral activation corresponding to the activity of the subject non-specific to the recognition itself. In this precise case, it is possible to choose a task in which one presents visual images with random motor responses. The activity thus recorded will thus correspond to the cerebral activity linked to visual perception, the programming of motor responses, and the activity of subjects between the assays. Thus, one subtracts this activity from the activity recorded in the first task. The activity that results from this subtraction is, in principle, that which corresponds to only face recognition. The difficulty of this method thus lies in the choice of the control task: the processes studied must have been the object of solid hypotheses to define those that are not the target of the study, even though they occur during the task.

(c) *Advantages and disadvantages*

In the 1980s, PET represented an undoubted advance because of its good spatial resolution of this technique (4 to 8 mm) in comparison to EEG—thus the only method of functional imagery. It made it possible in fact to map the cerebral flow, and thus indirectly cerebral activity, in the entire brain. Nevertheless, the disadvantages of this method are numerous and significant. Apart from the high cost of the equipment, it is in effect an invasive method, requiring several injections, and its temporal resolution is very weak (of the order of a minute), which does not allow the study of the dynamics of cerebral activations. Moreover, the need to apply the subtractive method limits the experimental protocols susceptible of being the object of the study of a PET. In fact, the advent of fMRI led to the gradual abandonment of PET.

3.2.2 fMRI

fMRI arose from anatomic magnetic resonance imaging (aMRI), conceived in 1970 to study the constituents of cerebral tissue.

(a) *Magnetic resonance*

It is based on the magnetic properties of hydrogen, one of the most numerous constituents of biological tissues, and thus of the cerebral tissue. The nucleus of the hydrogen atom comprises a single proton that possesses a magnetic moment, that is, it behaves like a small magnet (this phenomenon is called *spin*). The spins of hydrogen nuclei orient themselves naturally in a random manner so well that the magnetic moment, resulting from all the hydrogen atoms of a given region, is nil. But, if these spins are placed in a powerful external magnetic field, they will orient themselves in the direction of this field—this is *magnetization*.[8] In these conditions, the resulting magnetic moment is no longer nil. If one sends to it at the same time an impulse of radiofrequency lasting a very short time, the spins thus excited "enter into resonance" and align themselves according to a direction other than that of the general magnetic field. This is *magnetic resonance*. When this impulse is stopped, the atoms return to their original direction by restoring the energy accumulated: this is called *relaxation*. It produces a recorded signal, treated and converted into images by a powerful calculator. This signal depends on the quantity of spins and thus of the richness of tissues in the hydrogen atom: according to whether these are in the water, fats, muscles, or air, the quantity of energy released varies.

---

[8] According to the principle of a compass, where if one places a slightly magnetized needle that orients itself in the direction of the magnetic field created by the earth.

Thus, grey matter and white matter do not comprise the same quantity of hydrogen atoms, restoring (or returning) different quantities of energy for a single magnetic field and a single impulse of radiofrequency. The international unit by which the intensity of a magnetic field is quantified is the tesla (T).

Magnetic resonance has been used, from the 1970s onward, to generate highly precise images of the brain (anatomic **MRI** or aMRI).

(b) *The equipment*

The equipment is a sort of tunnel containing a horseshoe-shaped magnet producing a magnetic field and a bobbin emitting a radio wave of precise frequency. The magnetic field and radio wave are controlled by the experimenter. This field is also provided with antennae that record the resonance wave when the radio wave is suddenly interrupted. As with **PET**, the subject is in a lying-down position (see Fig. 3.3).

(c) *fMRI*

fMRI is based on the naturally magnetic properties of haemoglobin,[9] which differ slightly according to whether this molecule is linked to oxygen or otherwise. The synaptic activity consumes oxygen, which leads to a local increase in blood flow: this is the **BOLD** (blood oxygen level-dependent) response. In effect, the input of oxygen necessary for this activity is possible only by means of the increase of blood circulation, which results from vasodilation of surrounding arterioles. The blood thus brought near the active synapses is charged with oxygen. In other words, it is rich in oxyhaemoglobin. It must be noted that the **BOLD** response is detectable only for some hundreds of milliseconds after the synaptic activity. After that, the blood, which is discharged of its oxygen, increases in deoxyhaemoglobin concentration before it returns to normal.

Using fMRI it is possible to visualize the contrasts between the regions in which the blood flow increases, which are thus rich in oxyhaemoglobin, and the regions in which the blood flow does not vary, by means of the magnetic properties of the iron contained in the haemoglobin. In fact, the oxyhaemoglobin (iron associated with oxygen) is diamagnetic, while the deoxyhaemoglobin is paramagnetic. When the subject is placed in the equipment generating the magnetic field, each molecule of deoxyhaemoglobin causes a local disturbance of the homogeneity of the magnetic field, which leads to dephasing of spins and reduces the **MRI** signal. When there is cerebral activation, these small heterogeneities of the magnetic field are

---

[9] Haemoglobin is said to be paramagnetic.

reduced and the MRI signal increases. The deoxyhaemoglobin is thus an endogenous magnetic tracer.

(d) *Advantages and disadvantages*

Unlike PET, fMRI is a non-invasive method since it uses an endogenous signal. Its spatial resolution is high (of the order of a micron for aMRI and of millimetres for fMRI). Its temporal resolution is of the order of some hundreds of milliseconds, obviously of much lower quality than that of PET. It is thus an excellent method for visualization of the brain in activity, but it cannot be used to follow in detail the temporal organization of cerebral activities in association with the progression of cognitive processes.

Since the equipment is very costly, only some research centres have it. It must be noted that the more powerful the magnets, the higher the cost. The finesse of measures of active brain require much more powerful magnets than those required for aMRI.

Moreover, the position of the subject and the noise generated by the apparatus (despite the wearing of ear plugs) places the subject in a degree of discomfort. This could render examination impossible in claustrophobic subjects.

Finally, from an experimental point of view, the apparatus and the "tunnel" constitute a strong constraint for the realization of experimental protocols. For example, the presentation of visual stimuli requires complex systems for looking at images through a system of mirrors.

In conclusion, if EEG and MEG are methods of choice for chronometry of mental operations characteristic of cognitive functions, fMRI is undoubtedly adequate for the location of active cerebral structures. The future lies in a combination of these two types of methods.

4

High-level Perception: Vision

Perception of the environment is the result of a series of transformations operating at various levels of the nervous system and particularly at the cerebral level. Sensory signals are transformed into "percepts" that are integrated and then interpreted into significant entities. All the stimulations that come from our sense organs do not become "significant information." There are filters at various levels in which the attention processes play an essential role. For example, if we walk on a very busy street, our visual system is solicited by a multitude of visual stimuli that we perceive in a fleeting manner. We are not capable of saying what shops we walked in front of, or describing the appearance of people we passed. Still, at a given moment, in the middle of this multitude of visual stimulations, we will notice an object in a window or recognize a person in the crowd. This is the result of attention processes and mnesic processes (to recognize someone we must have a representation of that person in our memory) and shows that perceptive processes are linked, at least partly. This chapter is limited, nevertheless, to perceptive processes in the strict sense: low-level processes from the sense organs to the sensory cortex and high-level processes from the primary areas to the associative areas. Since we cannot address the entire perceptive environment, we have made the choice of treating only the case of visual perception, taking into account the place of vision in our understanding of the world, the complexity of visual processes, and the richness of knowledge available on this subject.

4.1 FROM SENSORY ORGAN TO SENSORY CORTEX[1]

Recall that visual stimulus is light, electromagnetic energy emitted in the form of waves. The quantity of energy emitted varies in proportion to the frequency of the wave and in inverse proportion to the length of the wave. Light emitted in high frequencies (with short wavelength) such as blue have a high degree of energy, unlike light of low frequency (red). Thus, all that we see results from the interpretation of messages that are only, at first, electromagnetic energy. This energy, coming from the eye, stimulates the cells of the retina, which gives rise to nervous messages that translate this visual stimulation.

4.1.1 The Eye

The eye is the optic compartment of vision. It is an organ in which the various elements allow light rays to focus in the retina to form a "retinal image". On its circumference there are three membranes (from the outside to the inside: the sclerotic, the choroid, and the retina) and on the interior three transparent mediums (aqueous humour, crystalline, and vitreous humour).

—The pupil is an orifice that allows light rays to enter the eye and reach the retina; its diameter of opening adapts to the quantity of light by means of a circular muscle (the iris that surrounds it).

—The cornea (transparent outer membrane that covers the pupil and iris), by its curvature, helps refract light rays that hit it so that they converge on the retina.

—The crystalline (biconvex lens composed of concentric lamellae) completes the action of the cornea in deviating the light rays issuing from points close to the eye; it is the ciliary muscles that allow the crystalline to increase its

---

[1] For more details on this part, we may usefully consult the work of Jean-Didier Baagot, *Information, Sensation, Perception*, "Cursus" series, Armand Colin. With respect to the anatomy of the eye and the retina and visual fields, we do not show a figure here, since the student can consult the many illustrations available on the internet.

curvature. This is the phenomenon of *accommodation*. The power of accommodation of the crystalline diminishes with age, passing from some centimetres in the child to several tenths of centimetres in the adult and during the process of aging. This is the phenomenon of *farsightedness*.

—The aqueous humour is a liquid situated behind the cornea. With tears secreted on the surface by the blinking of eyelids, it ensures the metabolism of the cornea deprived of blood vessels. It contributes also, by its refraction index, to the deviation of light rays towards the retina.

—The vitreous body (or vitreous humour) is a gelatinous fluid within the eye that keeps the retina attached to the choroid.[2]

—The corneal membrane is extended to the sclerotic (the white of the eye), the closing of which ensures the protection of the eye and in which are inserted three pairs of extraocular muscles that ensure the movements of the ocular globe.

—The choroid is an internal membrane attached to the sclerotic. Its richness in blood vessels allows it to nourish the iris and retina.

—The retina is a third membrane (the innermost, stuck to the choroid) comprising several layers of cells, hit by light rays that have crossed the optic compartment of the eye. The central region of the retina is called the *fovea*.

4.1.2 Structure of the Retina

It is at the retina that light energy is transformed into neural messages. The retina comprises three principal layers of cells (separated by intermediary layers) as follows, from the innermost to the outermost: apart from a primary layer comprising the external segments of photoreceptors sensitive to light, the external nuclear layer that contains the cellular bodies of photoreceptors, the internal nuclear layer that contains the bipolar cells, and finally the layer of ganglionic cells. The intermediary layers of horizontal cells and amacrine cells connect between them several cells of a single layer. The receptor fields of cells of these different layers become complexified to the extent that information progresses. Finally, each layer is the object of convergence

---

[2] With age, the vitreous body becomes more liquid: this causes sometimes the effect of seeing flying gnats (floating bodies); in certain cases, pieces of the vitreous body detach, causing "black spots" in the visual field corresponding to zones in which the retina is no longer attached to the choroid.

of information from the preceding layer, since there are around 125 million photoreceptors for 1 million ganglionic cells for each eye.

(a) *Photoreceptors*

Photoreceptors comprise an external segment made up of a stack of discs composed of photopigments, an internal segment, a cellular body and an axonic termination. It is the absorption of light energy by photopigments that generates modifications of the potential of the membrane of the photoreceptor with liberation of a neurotransmitter (at present, it is thought to be glutamate) by the photoreceptors. This is called *phototransduction*. In a curious manner, the photoreceptors liberate less glutamate in light than in dark. There are two types of photoreceptors: cones and rods. They differ notably in terms of the type of photopigment (three types in cones and thus three types of cones, and a single type in the rods) and in the number of discs of photopigments (much more numerous in rods than in cones). Thus, the rods are sensitive to much weaker light intensities (because of the quantity of photopigments they contain) than are the cones, while the latter are sensitive to different wavelengths depending on the photopigment they contain, which is not the case with rods, which contain only one type. While the cones are numerous at the centre of the retina, as we go further toward the periphery of the retina the rods are more numerous. Cones are responsible for precise and coloured vision, in central vision, when there is a large amount of light (photopic vision), while rods are responsible for night vision, of poorly lit visual stimuli projected at the periphery of the retina (scotopic vision). The receptor field of a photoreceptor is made up of a small portion of the visual field.

(b) *Bipolar cells*

After phototransduction operating at the level of photoreceptors, information is transmitted to the layer of bipolar cells. In fact, photoreceptors are in contact on the one hand with bipolar cells (direct pathway of transmission of information from photoreceptors to ganglionic cells) and on the other hand with horizontal cells that themselves put several bipolar cells into contact with each other (indirect pathway). Note that in the foveal region a bipolar cell receives its information from a single cone, and the information it transmits is thus highly precise information, while at the periphery of the retina a bipolar cell receives information from several thousands of rods, and the information it transmits is not very precise. Each bipolar cell has a receptor field (the photoreceptor or photoreceptors that are linked to it) in circular form, the illumination of the centre of which causes the inverse phenomenon of the illumination of its periphery (its circumference) by means of the layer of horizontal cells. The bipolar cells are linked directly to a set of photoreceptors and, at the same time, indirectly by horizontal cells, to photoreceptors located on the circumference of the region connected directly. The role of these horizontal cells is to inhibit the activity of neighbouring cells. This is the phenomenon of *lateral inhibition*.

There are two types of bipolar cells according to their response to glutamate liberated by photoreceptors: "on" cells that depolarize when the light hits the centre of their receptor field (little glutamate liberated by photoreceptors) and hyperpolarize when the light hits the periphery of this receptor field, and "off" cells, which function in the reverse manner. This phenomenon allows the accentuation of contrast between the sensory signal emanating from a precise region of the visual field and the signal emanating from nearby regions (all around). There is thus, at this level, a strict topographic organization that makes a precise point of the visual field correspond to a precise point on the retina and to a precise bipolar cell. Note that the bipolar cells thus stimulated do not emit action potential but only emit graduated potentials.

(c) *Ganglionic cells*

Unlike photoreceptors and bipolar cells, the ganglionic cells that receive their information from bipolar cells emit action potentials. Their axons constitute the optic nerve that transmits the information towards higher levels. The region of the retina in which these axons are grouped are deficient in photoreceptors and constitute what is called a "blind spot" (or Mariotte spot): the light that comes to this place is not perceived. The organization of receptor fields of ganglionic cells (with opposition between the centre and the periphery) is identical to that which has been described for bipolar cells, so that the accentuation of contrasts between neighbouring regions is preserved and amplified at the level of ganglionic cells then transmitted by the optic nerve.

Moreover, there are two major types of ganglionic cells: 90% of them are small P cells (from the Latin *parvus* or small), more frequent at the centre of the retina, and 5% of them are large M cells (from the Latin *magnus* or large). There are also 5% of cells that are not M or P, still poorly understood, more frequent at the periphery of the retina. The properties of these two types of cells are different: M cells have larger receptor field, more rapid propagation of action potential, and sensitivity to lower contrasts of light intensity than do P cells. Moreover, the response of M cells is of the "phasic" type, while that of P cells is of the "tonic" type throughout the duration of the stimulation. The M cells are particularly sensitive to movement of light stimulus, while the P cells are sensitive to differences in wavelength of light. These P cells mostly have "simple opposition of colour". They respond to a distinct colour delivered at the centre of their receptor field (red/green, blue/yellow). Finally, all the characteristics of P cells render them particularly sensitive to the form and to details of light stimulus. Thus, the information transmitted by the ganglionic cells (M and P) is already particularly treated in terms of light/dark, red/green, yellow/blue, mobile/immobile stimulus.

4.1.3 Pathways of Transport of Visual Information from Retina to Cortex

From the two retinas, messages are transmitted towards the cortex after having been relayed at the lateral geniculate body. In fact, they are transported differently according to the region from which they enter the visual field.

(a) *The visual field*

In the absence of movements of eyes and/or head, our field of vision is limited. In fact, each eye has its own visual field and only the central part of these two visual fields is common and forms the binocular field. Note that the image emanating from one eye is not exactly the same as that which emanates from the other, and it is the superposition—and interpretation by the brain—of the difference between these two images that is the basis of depth perception of the field.

Two parts can be distinguished in the retina of each eye: the nasal part and the temporal part. The light rays that hit them do not issued from the same portion of the visual field.

—The right nasal retina receives what comes from the temporal part of the right monocular visual field and the right part of the binocular field.

—The left nasal retina receives what comes from the temporal part of the left monocular visual field and the left part of the binocular field.

—The left temporal retina receives what comes from the centre of the visual field as well as what comes from the right part of the binocular field.

—The right temporal retina receives what comes from the centre of the visual field as well as what comes from the left part of the binocular field.

(b) *The optic chiasma and optic tractus*

Beyond the retina, information is transmitted by optic nerves that reunite at the optic chiasma located at the base of the brain, just before the hypophysis. At this level, the axons coming from the nasal retina pass from the other side (what is called *decussation of pathways*), while the axons coming from the temporal retina pursue their transport on the same side. The decussation of visual pathways is thus partial. The nasal retina receives information from the ipsilateral visual hemifield, while the temporal retina receives information from the controlateral visual hemifield. Partial decussation is thus manifested in the fact that the axons pursue their route beyond the optic chiasma—in pathways that are called *optic tractus*—in the following manner:

—The right optic tractus carries information issued from the left visual field to the right cerebral hemisphere.

—The left optic tractus carries information issued from the right visual field to the left cerebral hemisphere.

(c) *The lateral geniculate body (LGB)*

The LGB, which is located in the right part of the thalamus, receives 80% of fibres of the optic tractus. This is a set of six layers of cells, filled around the optic tractus in the form of a "knee", which differ in their type of cells as well as in the information they receive.

The right LGB receives information from the left visual hemifield via the left nasal retina and the right temporal retina, and the inverse is true of the left LGB. Information coming from the ipsilateral eye reaches layers 2, 3 and 5, while information from the controlateral eye reaches layers 1, 4 and 6. Thus, the six layers receive information from the same region of the visual field. The most ventral layers contain large cells that receive information from ganglionic M cells, while the dorsal layers are constituted of small cells that receive information from ganglionic P cells. Moreover, the receptor fields of LGB cells are organized in a concentric manner, like those of cells of the retina (with the same type of opposition).

Thus, information of different types (precise vision of visual stimulation, perception of movement of visual stimulus) is transported to the LGB and treated in parallel by parvocellular and magnocellular geniculo-striate pathways.

That being so, the information issuing from the retina constitutes only part of the excitatory connections of the LGB. Other excitatory connections come from the primary visual cortex itself, which, because of this, exerts a significant retroaction probably modulating the information coming from the retina.

(d) *Other relays*

Ten per cent of the optic nerve fibres are directed towards the upper colliculus (upper part of the mesencephalus tectum). This retino-tectal pathway is implicated in the orientation of sight when the eye is solicited by a stimulus at the periphery of the visual field. The neurons of the upper colliculi are then directed towards the subcortical structures, towards the LGB, or towards the pulvinar.

A small part of the optic nerve fibres are directed towards the pulvinar, nucleus of the posterior region of the thalamus, which also receives projections from the LGB. It is considered to be a centre of interpretation of visual images in playing a role in visual perception as well as in perception of movement. Its efferent fibres project on the visual areas implicated in the detection of movement of the extra-striate cortex. Thus, it probably plays a significant role in visual attention.

The remaining fibres of the optic nerve are directed toward other structures:

—The suprachiasmatic nerve of the hypothalamus, which is thus constantly informed about the ambient light and dark and plays an essential role in the regulation of our internal biological clock.

—The pretectum, which is located in the mesencephalus and controls the diameter of opening of the pupil.

4.1.4 The Primary Visual Cortex

From the LGB, the signals are transmitted to the visual cortex by pathways designated as optic radiations. Like all the sensory and motor cortices, the visual cortex is organized hierarchically: a primary (or striate) cortex and secondary cortices—still called *extra-striate cortices*—(monosensory associative areas). The information from secondary visual areas then converge towards the associative areas for a global treatment where information from other sensory modalities is associated.

The visual cortex (see Fig. 4.1) is organized into several concentric areas (at present numbering about 30), the first of which is the primary visual area or striate cortex (V1 or Brodmann area 17).

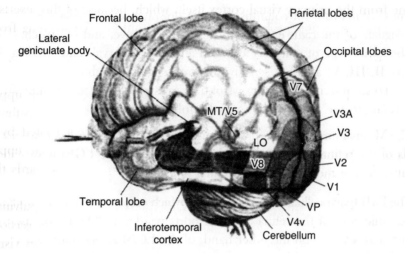

Fig. 4.1 The visual areas. V1: Primary area of striate cortex. V2, V3, ...
Extra-striate cortex.

Located in the most posterior part of the occipital lobe around the calcarine fissure (visible on a sagittal section between the two hemispheres), V1 is the area of reception of sensory signals from the geniculo-striate pathway.

The six layers of cells of the V1 are distinguished by the type of neurons they contain and their connections. Layer I contains the axons and dendrites of other layers. Layer IV is a receptor: its star-shaped cells receive signals from the LGB. Layers II, V and VI are emitters: their pyramidal cells send very long axons out of the primary visual cortex. Layer IV is itself broken down into stages that separately receive the signals emanating from parvo- and magnocellular pathways of the geniculo-striate pathway.

The successive works of Hubel and Wiesel (1962, 1968, 1977)[3] carried out on animals are source of our comprehension of the detailed organization of the striate cortex. Apart from the organization into typical layers of the cortex, Layer VI is organized into columns according to the principle of a retinotopy,[4] with a superpresentation of the fovea: the neurons of a column respond to a characteristic (orientation) of a point of the visual field. Finally, this organization into layers and columns is completed by the existence of

---

[3] Hubel and Wiesel received the Nobel Prize in medicine in 1981 for their description of the organization of the striate cortex.

[4] Retinotopy is a topographic organization according to which two adjacent points of the retina send signals by two groups of neurons adjacent to two adjacent points of the cortex. This topographic organization is a general principle of all the primary sensory and motor areas.

"bands" of neurons (or columns of ocular dominance) receiving alternatively the signals of the right eye and those of the left eye, and of "patches" or blobs (other type of columns localized at regular intervals and crossing the layers II, III, V, and VI) sensitive to wavelengths of light.

To summarize, the pathways of transmission of light information from the retina to the striate cortex are the following:

—The M canal (magnocellular), which originates in the magnocellular ganglionic cells of the retina and carries (via layers 1 and 2 of the LGB) information relative to the movement of the visual object.

—The P-IB (parvocellular-interblobs) canal, which originates in the parvocellular ganglionic cells of the retina and transports (via layers 3 and 5 on the one hand, and 4 and 6 on the other hand, of the LGB) information relative to the shape of visual objects.

—The canal of patches that originates in ganglionic cells that are not P or M and transport (via layers 1 and 4 on the one hand and 2 and 3 on the other hand of the LGB) information relative to the colour of visual objects.

The information is thus transmitted and treated in parallel, which allows simultaneous recording in the primary visual cortex of all the characteristics of the visual signal. This also permits information on the third dimension of space (information on depth), the signal emanating from one eye not being exactly the same as that emanating from the other eye for a single visual object.

4.2 FROM STRIATE CORTEX TO ASSOCIATIVE AREAS: THE "WHERE" AND "WHAT" PATHWAYS

The visual striate cortex is surrounded by the extra-striate cortex: secondary area (V2), associative areas (V3, V4, V5 or MT, PO, etc.). Layer VI sends a high proportion of its connections to the secondary visual cortex (V2, corresponding to the Brodmann areas 18 and 19), of which the neurons have properties similar to those of the neurons of V1 but of which some are distinguished. In fact, past the V1 stage, the principle of retinotopy is no longer respected and the rule becomes the convergence of afferences and divergence of efferences.

Although all of the details of the transmission of visual signals in the maze of the 30 or so visual areas beyond the striate cortex are not known, since the works of Ungerleider and Mirshkin (1982) some data are available in favour of a transmission depending on two major bundles:

–The inferior longitudinal bundle or ventral pathway that is directed towards the temporal lobe and treats of the nature and identification of the object ("what" pathway).

–The superior longitudinal bundle or dorsal pathway, which is directed towards the parietal lobe and treats of the position of the object ("where" pathway).

But it is important to emphasize that there are interconnections between these two bundles.

Shown initially by experiments of unitary recording of neurons by implanted electrodes carried out on animals, the existence of these two pathways has been confirmed in man by the study of patients and by experiments based on cerebral images.

4.2.1 Neurons with Different Physiological Properties

In the ape, it has been shown that parietal neurons (dorsal pathway) are activated by a light illuminating a determined region of space. Only 40% of them have receptor fields corresponding to the fovea, while the remaining 60% have receptor fields corresponding to the periphery of the retina. These last detect the entry of a visual stimulus in the peripheral visual field, which is compatible with the existence of a "where" pathway passing through these neurons of the dorsal pathway. The V5 area (or MT for middle temporal) is located in the median part of the temporal lobe. It is organized in columns (like V1) of detection of the direction of light stimulus. These afferences come from V2, V3 and the stage of layer IV of V1 integrated in the magnocellular pathway implicated in the movements of light stimulus. Beyond that are located other areas of analysis of movement of stimulus such as MST area, the cells of which are sensitive to various types of displacement: linear, circular, from one point to another.

On the contrary, the receptor fields of neurons of the infero-temporal region (ventral pathway) are broad and include always the foveal region. Their response is generally independent of the precise location of the stimulus in the visual field. The research of Grosse et al. (1972) and Desimone et al. (1984) allowed the identification, in macaque, of neurons in the infero-temporal region, at the level of the superior temporal sulcus and of the inferior temporal gyrus, responding selectively to complex forms such as a hand or a face (see Fig. 4.2). Thus, the response of neurons activated by a stimulus representing a hand considerably diminishes to the extent that the form of the stimulus is far from that of a hand.

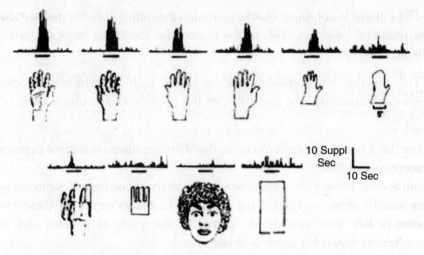

Fig. 4.2 Unitary recording of the response of a neuron of the infero-temporal cortex in the ape. According to Desimone et al. (1984), the neuron responds to the presentation of a hand or to stimuli strongly resembling a hand. It does not respond to the presentation of a face or a rectangle.

4.2.2 The "What" Hypothesis of the "Grandmother Cell" versus "Distributed Coding"

From the observation of neurons responding selectively to complex stimuli, the hypothesis has been put forth that, from the striate cortex to the infero-temporal cortex, neurons respond selectively to increasingly complex stimuli (hierarchical theory of perception) and that, in conclusion, a very limited number of neurons become active and respond specifically each time one sees or imagines a hand, an object, a particular face, etc. This hypothesis has been called the *grandmother cell hypothesis* or coding by "gnostic units".

But this hypothesis does not stand up to some arguments. In effect, a considerable number of gnostic units would be needed for all possible objects, for all the possible views under different angles of all these objects. Moreover, the recognition of a particular object becomes impossible on the death of a specific neuron of perception of a particular object. In the same manner, the perception of a new object will become impossible. Finally, the response of a neuron is not constant and, above all, such cells have never actually been found (recall that the neuron described previously responds to a hand but also to other figures more or less resembling ·a hand).

In these conditions, the hypothesis of "coding of populations" or "distributed coding" has been substituted for the hypothesis of grandmother cell. According to this hypothesis, a single neuron may become active in very different situations. The coding of a particular object will demand the activity of a large assembly of neurons widely distributed in the visual areas, each of these neurons not being specific to this object. This hypothesis is much more compatible with the multiplicity of visual objects and possible points of view; it resolves the problem of perception of new objects or perception after neuronal death. It can also explain false recognition: the confusion between a new face and a known face comes from the activation of a significant proportion of neurons implicated in the recognition of a known face because of characteristics common to the two faces.

Nevertheless, the function of such networks and the manner in which the perception of an object emerges in a coherent whole is still debated. Certainly, visual perception will be possible because of parallel treatment from the different layers, columns and patches of the striate cortex up to the infero-temporal cortex, the "link" being ensured by the numerous horizontal connections of layer III of the cortex that will relate the different areas treating of diverse characteristics of the visual object. Besides, the emergence of the perception of an object will result from the synchronous activation of populations of neurons present in different regions. This synchronization will constitute the "cementing" of a perception into a coherent whole of distinct elements treated as such by the visual system.

4.2.3 The "Where" and "What" Pathways in Humans

The first confirmations of the existence of these two pathways in humans came from the observation of patients (for review see Sieroff, 2004). Patient LM, described by Zihl et al. (1983), following a bilateral lesion of the occipito-lateral white matter and of the middle temporal (corresponding to V5 or MT in the macaque), had difficulties in perceiving the movement and speed of visual objects (akinetopsy) but did not have trouble recognizing even visual objects and faces. Besides, his problem did not involve the movements of auditory or somesthesic stimuli. On the contrary, patient DF, described by Goodale and Milner (1992), presented bilateral lesions at the occipital level and above all at the infero-temporal level. Despite correct visual acuity, DF could not name an object that she could otherwise describe, when this object was presented to her visually. On the other hand, she could identify and name the object when it was placed in her hand. These two cases, and others, illustrate certain deficits associated with specific damage to the dorsal pathway (LM) and the ventral pathway (DF).

Experiments in brain imaging have also yielded evidence of the existence of these two pathways in humans.

For example, in a PET experiment, Haxy et al. (1991) compared cerebral activations during the course of three tasks (see Fig. 4.3).

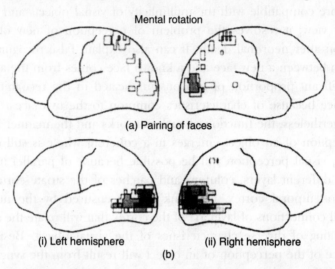

Mental rotation

(a) Pairing of faces

(i) Left hemisphere   (ii) Right hemisphere
(b)

Fig. 4.3 The "where" and "what" in humans (Haxby et al., 1991). A PET experiment. Above, task of pairing geometric figures (the task involves a mental rotation); the activated regions correspond to the visual cortex (occipital lobe) and to the dorsal pathway (of "where", parietal lobe). Below, task of pairing visual objects (faces); the activated regions correspond to the visual cortex (occipital lobe) and the ventral pathway (of "what", infero-temporal cortex).

—A test of face recognition using faces from the test of Benton and Van Allen (1973): three faces are presented in three squares arranged in a triangle. the subjects must indicate (by pressing the right button with the right index finger or a left button with the left index finger) whether the face presented on top corresponds with the bottom right face or the bottom left face.

—A test of spatial location: on the same principle, three squares are presented, each containing a point and two lines. The subjects must indicate which square at the bottom corresponds to that at top, knowing that in a bottom square, the arrangement of the point and lines is the same as in the top square but that it has been rotated 90, 180 or 270°, while in the other bottom square, the arrangement of the point and lines is different from that of the top square. Thus, the subjects must make a mental rotation to find the correct answer.

—A control test that allows isolation (by subtraction) of cerebral activation linked to tasks of recognition or spatial localization of cerebral activations linked to the motor response: three empty squares arranged as before are presented to the subjects, who must press alternatively on the right and left buttons.

Their data from the PET showed an activation of the lateral occipital cortex in the two visual tasks. Moreover, the task of face recognition activated the inferior region of the occipito-temporal cortex located anterior to the occipital region activated by the two patches. The patch of spatial localization activated a lateral region of the superior parietal cortex.

This experiment thus marked the beginning of the confirmation of the existence in humans, as in the ape, of the implication of the medial inferior temporal cortex in the recognition of objects (ventral pathway) and that of the parietal cortex (dorsal pathway) in the location of visual stimulus in space.

4.2.4 Organization of Ventral and Dorsal Pathways

A large number of experiments carried out on animals and humans, notably by the Haxby research team, have subsequently come to enrich the knowledge of the organization of these two pathways and of their reciprocal relationships. It arises from this that although the existence of these two pathways is not contestable, their respective roles and most of all their mutual relationships are probably highly complex.

In the first place, the segregation between the signals issuing from the parvo- and magnocellular pathways persists all along the ventral and dorsal pathways: the P-IB canal feeds the ventral pathway, while the M canal feeds the dorsal pathway.

Recall, moreover, that the pathways of treatment of information are the object of feedback: the information treated to the extent of relays and areas in return sends information on the preceding relays and areas. All the same, particular relays of colliculi and of the pulvinar have been indicated that have maintained reciprocal connections with the pathways of treatment of the information. Thus, the tecto-pulvinar system maintains reciprocal relationships with the extra-striate cortex.

If one takes again the case of the patient DF mentioned previously, Goodale and Milner (1992) showed that the aperceptive visual agnosy that she suffered did not hinder nor correctly direct her hand toward an object that she was asked to hold, nor to orient her wrist correctly as, for example, to slide a card that she holds in her hand into a slot in an immobile object presented in front of her or to direct her fingers correctly to seize this object. In the absence of any real movement on her part or of the object itself, this shows that DF has a non-conscious form of recognition of the visual object. Her problem thus pertains to the *conscious* representation of the form of the object. Thus, the ventral pathway is above all the pathway of *conscious recognition* of the identity of visual objects.

The dorsal pathway comprises several cortical regions:

–The middle temporal area (MT or V5) and the parieto-occipital area (PO), also called V6-V6A, located on the border of the parieto-occipital groove for the first stages.

–The superior middle temporal (SMT) and the ventral and lateral intraparietal areas (VIP and LIP) for the subsequent stages.

The V5 area (or MT), located in the middle part of the temporal lobe, is organized into columns (like V1) of detection of the direction of light stimulus. Its afferences come from V2, V3, and the stage of the layer IV of V1, integrated in a magnocellular pathway implicated in the movements of light stimulus. Beyond that are located other areas of analysis of movement of stimulus such as the SMT area, the cells of which are sensitive to various types of displacement, such as linear, circular, or from one point to another. Moreover, the connections between MT on the one hand and V2, V3, V4 on the other are reciprocal. All the same, the parieto-occipital (PO) aera, specialized in the spatial location, maintains reciprocal connections with V2.

In conclusion, not only does the dorsal pathway analyse the movement of visual stimulus, but also its analysis participates in the recognition of the visual object. Its roles are in effect multiple: to extract the pertinent information from a flow of objects that cross its visual field, to help the orientation of eye movement, to identify the objects that move around us, to guide our movements in the visual space. Thus, the movement of the visual object, in changing the visual information emanating from this object (shadows, contours, ...) participates in visual perception, the recognition of invariants of the object, and thus in its recognition. The dorsal pathway thus plays a virtual role in the guiding of our actions towards the visual objects of our environment as well as in their recognition.

This complexity of the organization of pathways of treatment of the visual information at the cerebral level explains the complexity of deficiencies consequent on focused lesions. For example, we can cite the case of patients incapable of recognizing static visual objects but finding their capacity of recognition when the object is moving. Moreover, some find this capacity for any type of movement of the object while others find it only when the movement of the object "mimics" its use (for example, a screw that turns). In the first case, the deficiency really concerns highly precocious processes implicated in the perception of contours, of forms with respect to the base, of the integration in three dimensions of an image presented in two dimensions, and the movement relevant to invisible portions of the object. In the second case, it is probably a matter of later processes of access to representations of the object in memory.

In a series of experiments, the research team of Thorpe (Fize et al., 2000; Van Rullen and Thorpe, 2001) studied concomitant cerebral activations of treatment of various types of visual objects (animals, vehicles inserted in diverse visual scenes) by fMRI and by EP. The others have thus shown activation of the following regions: right occipito-temporal groove and right and left parahippocampic gyri (Brodmann area 31 on the internal inferior surface) and a large part of the left fusiform gyrus and the medial occipital gyrus (Brodmann areas 19 and 37). Their study in EP demonstrated two distinct mechanisms of treatment. The first involved a precocious sensory treatment that survives 75 ms post-stimulus: it does not depend on the type of patch but depends on visual properties of stimuli and thus reflects a low-level treatment. The second survives 150 ms post-stimulus: linked to the type of patch, it is independent of physical characteristics of the stimulus and reflects thus a high-level treatment.

4.3 THE PECULIAR CASE OF FACE RECOGNITION

Among all visual objects, the face occupies a particular place. It plays a crucial role in social interactions: not only is it the principal vector of personal identity, fundamental in humans, but it also constitutes an essential vector of communication, of intentions, of emotions. The information carried by a face is thus of immense richness. We are capable of discriminating thousands of faces, memorizing an immense number of faces, identifying many of them by name, and so on. Besides, these capacities are hardly affected by the modifications of certain aspects such as addition of certain attributes (glasses, moustaches), hair style, or wrinkles. Moreover, contrary to the number of acquired competences, our capacity of face recognition develops throughout our lives: although one may lose certain capacities because of age, from lack of use,[5] this phenomenon does not affect the treatment of faces: the advance in age only increases the number of faces encountered and treated, so that our expertise in this field develops throughout our lives.

On the basis of these observations, numerous authors have thus offered the hypothesis that evolution will, in humans as well as in other higher primates in which social interactions are important, allow the development of treatment and recognition of specific and particularly important faces, calling on cerebral substrates and specific perceptive modules.

A group of experimental results pleads in favour of such specificity, whether by the study of patients or by behavioural studies or studies in brain imaging.

4.3.1 Prosopagnosy

In the domain of neuropsychology first of all, among the visual agnosies, there is one that is astonishing, prosopagnosy, which is the incapacity of patients to recognize familiar faces whereas they can describe the unrecognized face, recognize a person by his voice or clothes, but invariably respond "unknown" when only the face of this familiar person is presented to them (they are, moreover, also incapable of recognizing themselves in a mirror). These patients do not present an equivalent deficiency with respect to other visual objects. Nevertheless, this deficiency in itself does not suffice to show a specific system of treatment. In effect, it may be an intra-category deficiency of discrimination within a category of objects in which there is an infinity of examples and of which the informative content is much higher than that of other visual objects. McNeil and Warrington (1993) studied the case of a shepherd who was an expert in recognition of sheep and thus capable of recognizing each of his sheep as well as we can recognize the faces of people we know. These authors, by an adapted protocol, were able to show that this patient had lost the capacity to recognize known faces but not his capacity to recognize his sheep. They concluded that the dissociation certainly existed, and that the deficit of prosopagnosic patients could not be due to a simple problem of intra-categorial discrimination.

---

[5] People who have poor reading abilities and who have stopped exercising these abilities from the end of their school years lose their low competences and can be classified as illiterates after a few years.

Double dissociations also militate in favour of the hypothesis of a system of face recognition that is distinct from a system of recognition of other visual objects.

In his studies on associative agnosy, Farah (1990, 1994) recounted numerous cases of patients affected with one, two or three conditions, that is, visual agnosy of objects, prosopagnosy and alexia (for a description of these conditions, see Sieroff, 2004). This author showed that one can observe on the one hand patients affected by three types of agnosies, and on the other hand patients affected with only prosopagnosy or alexia, but no patient affected with only agnosy of objects. Moreover, if prosopagnosy can be associated with a visual agnosy of objects, it is never associated with alexia alone, without agnosy of objects. All the same, alexia can be associated with a visual agnosy of objects. This signifies probably that the association of three conditions comes from very extensive lesions but that the alexia on the one hand, and prosopagnosy on the other, result from modules of treatment that are mutually independent. On the other hand, these two troubles would not be independent of a more "basic" module of visual treatment of objects.

4.3.2 The Effect of Superiority of Faces

The effect of superiority of faces was demonstrated by Homa et al. (1976) in the following situation: three types of stimuli were presented to subjects (normal faces, faces with disordered features, and isolated features), at the end of which the subjects must draw on slides the traits that were presented to them. In these conditions, the traits were better recognized if they were previously presented in the context of a normal face (and not in the context of a disordered face). Thus, there is an effect of superiority of faces with respect to faces with mixed features or isolated features. Subsequently, this effect was observed again in other conditions. For example, Davidoff (1986) showed this effect using stimuli formed of a contour of a face with a single feature (eyes, mouth or nose), the two other characteristics being represented by objects (for example, a telephone receiver for the eyes). This author thus observed that the rate of recognition of features figured by objects did not differ as a function of type of face within which they were presented (normal or with mixed features). On the other hand, for the rate of recognition of normal traits, the result was consistent with that of the experiment of Homa et al. (1976). Davidoff (1986) also observed that a facial feature is best recognized when it is presented in a normal facial context in which the other traits figure explicitly and are not replaced by objects. These results are in favour of a representation in memory of the general configuration of faces including the position of features and their spatial interrelationships. This result was later confirmed, notably by Tanaka and Farah (1993) in varied tests.

The obvious question thus is whether such an effect concerns only faces or all visual objects. Davidoff and Donelly (1990) showed an effect of the same type by presenting chairs. Nevertheless, this effect of superiority of normal chairs over chairs in which the different parts were mixed is much less significant than in the case of faces. Moreover, it was observed only in some trials. Finally, while the recognition of "mixed" chairs remained good, the performance for facial recognition was so poor that not only did it not differ from that realized on isolated features, it was inferior to the performance for the "mixed" chairs. This pleads in favour of a specificity of treatment of faces with respect to other visual objects. This specificity rests in the configural treatment of faces based on holistic representation of faces that is not the simple addition of representation of facial features, which characterize the analytic treatment (feature by feature) that pertains to other visual objects.

Experiments in EP have come to reinforce these conclusions. For example, Botzel et al. (1989) observed a positive wave at the level of the vertex, around 200 ms after the presentation of visual stimulus (titled P2 Vertex or VPP for vertex positive potential) particularly ample after the presentation of faces, even in schematic form, while this wave was considerably reduced, even absent, after the presentation of other complex forms (trees, chairs, ...) or faces with completely disorganized features. All the same, George et al. (1996) showed the existence of negativities (N170) occurring in infero-temporal regions, around 170 ms after the presentation of stimulus, much more ample in the case of regular faces than in that of faces with mixed features (see Fig. 4.4).

On their part, Bentin et al. (1996) showed that these N170 were more ample and more precocious for normal faces than for faces with mixed features or features presented in isolation. Nevertheless, in this last case (isolated features), the N170 evoked by the eyes were greater than the N170 evoked by other features (nose or mouth).

All these data together suggest thus that the structural coding of faces, marked by infero-temporal N170, lies on the configuration of facial traits and of the face taken as a whole (configural, holistic treatment) but that, in this configuration, the eyes play a crucial role: the configuration and spatial relationships between the features could be evaluated with respect to eyes, a "dominant" trait in a face.

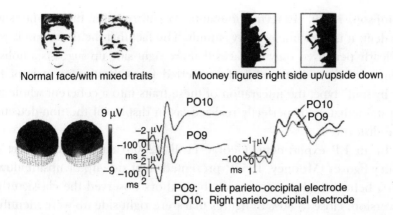

Normal face/with mixed traits   Mooney figures right side up/upside down

PO9: Left parieto-occipital electrode
PO10: Right parieto-occipital electrode

Fig. 4.4 Effect of superiority and effect of inversion of faces on the N170 (George et al., 1976, 2000). Left: effect of superiority of normal faces over faces with mixed features. Right: effect of inversion of Mooney figures. The evoked potential, recorded on right parieto-occipital electrodes (PO10) and left parieto-occipital electrodes (PO9), corresponds to normal faces (left part) and upside down faces (right part). At bottom left, map of cerebral activations of surface at the time when the N170 was recorded for normal faces: it is seen that the activity is greater on the right than on the left.

4.3.3 The Effect of Inversion

It is a well-known phenomenon that face recognition becomes difficult when the face is upside down. To find out whether this effect of inversion was specific to faces, Yin (1969, 1970) presented subjects with black and white photos right side up and inverted, of faces, houses, aeroplanes, and drawings of men in different postures and asked them to identify (recognize) what they saw. The photos of faces right side up were the best recognized, while the upside down photos of faces were the least recognized. The performances on other visual objects fell between these two extremes, with an effect of inversion present for the houses and silhouettes but less than for the faces. Among the numerous studies reporting this effect, it is interesting to note that the only studies in which it has not been observed concern tasks of pairing faces in which the mnesic factor is reduced, even non-existent. This effect of inversion would thus be linked to representations in memory.

Subsequently, other authors studied this effect by introducing distortions in certain traits. The distortion of traits with respect to the general configuration is not perceived on faces presented upside down (it is perceived only when the image is rotated 180°) and the response of subjects is thus less rapid

(Thompson, 1988).[6] In terms of quantity of information, the two faces are equivalent: it is the same sensory stimuli. The fact that the distortion is well and clearly perceived only for faces that are right side up suggests a holistic treatment of these faces, while for inverted faces the treatment is of the "trait by trait" type, the integration of these traits into a coherent whole not being immediately or perfectly realized, as in display of the non-detection of the distortion.

In an EP experiment, George et al. (2005) studied this effect on Mooney figures (Mooney, 1957)[7] presented right side up or upside down. From a behavioural point of view, the authors observed the classic effect of inversion: close to 80% of figures that were right side up were identified as faces, while the percentage fell to 20% for upside down figures. Moreover, the "face" responses were faster for right side up figures than for the upside down figures, while for "non-face" responses the response time was of the same order whether the figure was presented right side up or upside down. The examination of evoked potential revealed more ample N170 for figures identified as faces than for figures not identified as faces. They were also more ample for figures that were right side up than for inverted figures but only when the figures were recognized as faces: the effect of inversion appeared on the N170 only when the figures were recognized as faces (see Fig. 4.4). Moreover, the authors noted asymmetries of cerebral activations between the two hemispheres calling on the hypothesis of a preferential implication of the right hemisphere for the treatment of faces, the left hemisphere taking in charge the perceptive characteristics of the stimulation.

Using the protocol of inversion with distortion on a previously described trait (Thompson, 1988) in a prosopagnosic patient, Farah (1994) showed that the performance of this patient was better for faces presented upside down than for faces presented right side up. In consequence, the system of perception and analysis of traits was preserved in this patient while his system of overall recognition was faulty, which corroborated the hypothesis of a specific model of face recognition.

---

[6] Thompson used the word *play* to title his study *Margaret Thatcher: A New Illusion*, and so the effect that he demonstrated is presently known as the "Thatcher effect".

[7] Highly dissymmetric photographs of faces in which only shadow (in black) and light (in white) are visible.

4.3.4 The Bruce and Young Model

Several cognitive models of face recognition have been elaborated (for review, see Bruyer, 1987). These models derived from models of shape recognition (Biederman, 1972), word recognition (Mortin, 1969), and object recognition (Warren and Morton, 1982). Bruce and Young proposed in1986 a model of treatment of faces that, although slightly improved by this team from an initial version, was not fundamentally modified. After a previous stage of classification of stimulus in the category "face", this model comprises three major steps. First, a series of perceptive analyses are realized on the face and generate a particular representation of the face: this is the stage of structural coding of the face. The invariant properties, whatever the modifications of presentation, of this face are extracted from this representation. Then, this representation is compared to representations stored in memory (the facial recognition units or FRU) and, finally, if they correspond to an existing representation, there is recognition: the face is considered familiar. It is then possible to access semantic information relative to the identity of the person (person identity node or PIN). It is only at the end that the person's name is generated. If these three steps (coding, FRU, PIN) constitute the framework of the model, operations parallel to and independent of the identification itself can be realized for extraction of other useful information such as sex, age of face during recognition, the movements of the mouth (to infer what it says), its facial expressions (to infer the emotion expressed). Note that the stage of generation of the name is not part, properly speaking, of this recognition model since it is true that one may perfectly recognize a face and know in what circumstances one has seen it, without immediately recollecting the name of the person (a very common phenomenon that increases with age).

Many experiments have shown, since the elaboration of this model, that the effects of inversion and superiority of faces was entirely coherent with this model.

4.3.5 The Underlying Networks of Face Recognition

We mentioned previously the case of patients suffering from prosopagnosy or alexia. The case of prosopagnosic patients reported in the literature involved bilateral lesions of the infero-temporal ventral cortex (Sergent and Signoret, 1992) and, in certain cases, the lesions of the same areas but only in the right hemisphere (de Renzi, 1986). To our knowledge, no case of prosopagnosy associated with a lesion only in the left hemisphere seems to have been reported. Alexia is found in patients suffering left lesions of the angular gyrus, which is located in the posterior part of the parietal lobe. The dissociation of these problems can be related to the dissociation of lesions that are associated with them: the ventral pathway (bilateral or right) for prosopagnosy, the left dorsal pathway for alexia.

(a) *The ventral pathway and conscious recognition*

It has been seen previously that the perceptive processes of the ventral pathway could be associated with conscious recognition. If such is the case, the deficit of prosopagnosic patients, or at least some of them, could concern only conscious recognition of familiar faces. In this regard, Renault et al. (1989) showed, using EP, a form of non-conscious recognition in a prosopagnosic patient. These authors applied the "oddball" protocol and the study of the P300 wave, particularly sensitive to the rarity of stimulus in this type of protocol, to a prosopagnosic patient by presenting him with celebrity faces (rare stimuli) and unknown faces (frequent stimuli). When the patient recognized none of the celebrity faces, his P300 evoked by these (rare stimuli of frequency 33%) was much greater than his P300 evoked by unknown faces (frequent stimuli, 66%). On the other hand, when the two types of stimuli were presented with a frequency of 50% each, the P300 evoked by the two types of stimuli did not vary. This variation of the P300 as a function of the rarity of the stimulus shows that the patient is sensitive to the bias of probability. Since the two types of stimuli varied only as a function of their degree of familiarity, this sensitivity to the bias of frequency of the P300 exists only if the patient has made the distinction between the two types of stimuli. As he consciously recognized no celebrity faces, it could only be concluded that this patient displayed a form of non-conscious recognition of celebrity faces that he declared he could not recognize.

(b) *Populations of neurons dedicated to facial recognition*

If the "grandmother" cell hypothesis, explaining a coding of perceptive treatment of visual objects, was rejected for the reasons outlined earlier, it must nevertheless be emphasized that numerous experiences show the existence of cells coding specifically for faces within the anterior temporal cortex of the macaque. According to Perret et al. (1982), these cells are located in various places of this portion of the cortex and will constitute notably 10% of the deepest part of the upper temporal groove; they are distributed in columns perpendicular to the surface of the cortex, thus forming some bands of some millimetres' width (Perret et al. 1985). In a series of studies, Perret's team thus demonstrated that these cells respond only to certain types of faces (real faces, photos, or even illustrations of faces) but do not respond to other complex stimuli (other visual objects) or to geometric form, or to destructured faces, or to isolated facial features. Reciprocally, disseminated within "face" cells, some cells seem to respond specifically to facial features (eyes, mouth). Finally, from the entire set of data accumulated on these very peculiar cells of the infero-temporal cortex, Perret et al. (1987) conclude that faces are treated, within the upper temporal groove, according to two processes. First, coding of traits seen under the angle of presentation intervenes, by cells specifically sensitive to these characteristics. This occurs at the same time as the activation of cells sensitive to the general configuration of the face as it is presented (from a certain angle). The response of these two types of cells activates the specific face cells of the face under this angle of view, which then activates the specific face cells of a particular face (no matter what the angle of view). Perret et al. (1987) propose that the treatment of faces calls on a distributed coding and at the same time a coding by gnostic units. Note that the hypothesis of distributed coding is backed up by numerous other studies. For example, for Young and Yamane (1992), "face" neurons within the anterior part of the infero-temporal cortex analyse the physical resemblances between faces, while properties such as familiarity (in other words, resemblance to facial representations in memory) are analyzed by "face" neurons of the upper temporal groove. There is distribution, within the anterior portion of the infero-temporal cortex and the upper temporal groove, of a network of treatment of faces by neurons of which one part will be specific to faces. Whether one agrees with the conclusions of Perret's team or Young's team, the specificity of treatment of faces by a population of neurons that are dedicated to it is retained in both cases.

(c) *The input of cerebral imaging for location of facial treatment networks*

In their experiment to show the effect of superiority of faces over faces with mixed features through the study of N170, George et al. (1996) showed that this effect is not limited to the temporal window of these waves. The differences of EP follow beyond the N170 and involved all the negativity that accompanies the treatment of faces (negativity of treatment). Later studies of the same research team made it possible to advance the hypothesis of the existence of a complex network implicating various ventral and lateral regions of the underlying temporal lobe to facial recognition. This network comprises notably the fusiform gyrus and the parahippocampic gyrus. Moreover, the N170 being generally more ample at right, but being nevertheless present at left, the networks of facial treatment will implicate both hemispheres, but the right hemisphere will predominate.

In an fMRI experiment, Haxby et al. (2001) sought to see whether a particular category of visual stimuli (faces, cats, trees...) evoked a specific configuration of activation in the ventral pathway that was different from configurations of activations for other stimuli. They found that the perception of different categories of visual objects activates extensive regions of the temporo-ventral cortex. There is a recovery of regions activated by faces and by other visual objects but, for each category of stimuli, there is a specific configuration of response of ventral temporal cortex: the regions activated are not exactly the same from one object to another. It should be noted that this specificity pertains to all the types of visual objects and not only faces or even biologically significant objects (e.g., animals). In fact, it all makes sense when one considers the quantity of activation. Small activities or submaximal responses are an integral part of the neuronal network. For one category of object there are significant responses of certain regions and weaker responses of neighbouring regions. But, for another category of object, one will find significant activity where there was little activity in the preceding case and weak activity where there was earlier a great deal. Finally, for one category of object one has a specific configuration of activities, that is, a set of maximal responses in certain regions and submaximal responses in others. For another category of object, however, we find the same regions active with a "balance" that is different between maximal activations and submaximal activations. According to Haxby et al. (2001), regions such as the para-hippocampic gyrus or the fusiform gyrus are not specific to a particular visual object (that is, a particular spatial arrangement of light stimuli) or human faces, but are rather part of a wider network dedicated to the representation of all visual objects and are more or less active according to the type of the object.

4.3.6 Interactions between Face Recognition and Recognition of Facial Emotions

The Bruce and Young model postulates the functional independence of processes of treatment of faces and of facial expression. The case of certain prosopagnosic patients sustains this independence since the literature reports cases of patients incapable of recognizing known faces but capable of recognizing the expression of a face (Bruyer, 1983) and the other way around (Kurucz and Feldmar, 1979).

Intracerebral recordings made in the case of the apes display the cells of the temporal cortex responding to a face and not responding to its expression and, on the contrary, cells responding to the facial expression without responding to the identity of the face (Desimone et al., 1984; Perret et al., 1984). Moreover, regions implicated in face recognition will be located in infero-temporal cerebral structures, including the fusiform gyrus, while the regions implicated in the recognition of facial emotions will be limited to cortical areas surrounding the upper temporal groove (Hasselmo et al., 1989).

For all that, these different localizations of systems of coding of faces on the one hand, and of facial expressions on the other hand, do not imply the total independence of these two systems and the absence of relationships and connections between the cerebral regions that underlie them. In fact, a large number of published data report facilitations in face recognition in relation with the emotion expressed by these faces, notably in the case of joy (Sansone and Tiberghien, 1993; Kaufmann and Schweinberger, 2004). On their side, Young et al. (1996) described the case of a patient DR, who had undergone a partial bilateral amygdalectomy, who did not recognize facial expressions but performed well when she had to pair faces by identity. Nevertheless, when the expression of the faces was manipulated, she failed to pair them. For this patient, two different expressions of a single face belonged to two different faces.

In the ape, Hasselmo et al. (1989) showed that certain neurons respond to identity and facial expression at the same time. All the same, in a study in PET realized in humans, Sergent et al. (1994) observed that if the blood flow increased in different regions for tasks of facial identification and recognition of expressions, other regions were more or less activated in the two tasks. In an EP study, Marinkovic and Halgren (1993) observed a lateral occipito-temporal wave, 200 ms after appearance of smiling or sad faces, which was absent when the expression of the faces was neutral, a wave that they interpreted in terms of a precocious influence of the facial expression on the processes of facial recognition, well before its identification.

On their part, Adolphs et al. (1994) advanced the hypothesis of an influence of the amygdalus on the extrastriate cortex, whereas the amygdalus is a structure of the temporal cortex responding essentially to emotional stimuli.

Finally, Haxby et al. (2000) proposed a model of face recognition in which a subsystem analyses the invariant aspects of a face (the fusiform gyrus), while another subsystem (the upper temporal groove) analyses its changing aspects, including its emotional expression. For these authors, the limbic structures treating of emotions, as well as the parietal regions implicated in the spatial orientation of attention, also participate in the perception of faces by treating certain information conveyed by the face. Thus, according to Haxby et al. (2000), the recruitment of these regions facilitates face recognition by treating its emotional expression as well as the direction of the glance and movements of the mouth since they are activated at the same time as the basic network of face recognition.

In conclusion, it is entirely clear that the underlying cerebral networks of face recognition and those that underlie the recognition of facial emotions interact. Even though they are still not totally elucidated, they seem closely specific to the system of treatment of faces vis-à-vis other visual objects. Facial recognition thus is based on extensive neuronal networks that go beyond the ventral and dorsal pathways of visual treatment.

5

Memory

Why do we have no trouble recalling very old memories while we sometimes (often, as we age) cannot remember what we did the day before? Why are we still able to ride a bicycle years after we last did so? Why do we often perfectly remember the face of a school friend, or events that occurred in her company, while we are entirely incapable of remembering her name? These surprising phenomena display the complexity of the organization of memory or, to be more precise, systems of memories.

5.1 DIFFERENT TYPES OF MEMORY

While learning encompasses the processes of acquisition of new information, memory corresponds to the persistence and retention of information and knowledge acquired by learning, throughout our lives. But there is not just a single form of learning, a single type of memory. Similarly, there is not just one place in which information is stored in the brain, nor is there a single type of biological trace (or engram) of what has been learned in neuronal networks.

The models of memory elaborated by psychologists teach us that the hypothetical stages of memory comprise the following: coding (the treatment of information with a view to their storage, that is, on the one hand the acquisition through sensory processes and on the other hand the consolidation that permits the construction of a representation), storage and recovery. Note that one can learn and know without being conscious of it.

Two fundamental distinctions characterize cognitive theories of memory: the duration of retention (whence the distinction between sensory or short-term memory and working or long-term memory) and the type of information stored in long-term memory.

5.1.1 Memory and Duration of Retention

(a) *Sensory memory*
Sensory memory is a form of automatic memory that does not depend on the field of consciousness; its form of representation is sensory. This sensory trace consecutive to stimulation is very brief; it lasts only some hundreds of milliseconds for the visual system (iconic memory) and two or three seconds for the auditory system (echoic memory).[1] Coding of information of this memory is similar to that of the original sensory experience of which it gives a faithful representation. Its capacity is very high and corresponds really to the capacity of reception and treatment of the sensory organ.

(b) *Short-term memory*
Short-term memory allows the retention of information in the course of treatment. Its capacity, or span, is limited (7 ± 2 items) but depends on the organization of the information. The representations there are semantic (at least in an elementary manner). According to the initial model of Atkinson and Schiffrin (1968), after passage into sensory memory, the items selected by the attentional processes are stored in short-term memory before being transferred into long-term memory if they can form the object of a mental repetition. At each step of these processes, there is loss of information by decline and/or by interference. In the more recent models, maintenance in short-term memory does not suffice for long-term memorization: also, there is intervention of factors such as depth of treatment during the coding and mental repetition, research into long-term memory that allows us to organize and treat information during the course of coding, establish semantic links between the new information and the old knowledge. To clarify, the information is not just maintained, it is processed. Baddeley and his team in 1974 introduced the concept of working memory, which lasts beyond the

---

[1] These two forms of sensory memory are the best known. But sensory memory also exists for tactile pressure (haptic memory), taste, and odour.

initial conception of a short-term memory conceived like a simple "buffer-memory" upstream of the long-term memory. There are actually several types of short-term memory corresponding to several storage sites, related to the support of presentation of the information (visual, auditory, etc.) and to the purpose of maintaining the information in long-term memory.

(c) *Working memory*

As its name indicates, working memory makes it possible to "work", that is, carry out a cognitive treatment, on information memorized temporarily. It is probably made up of several subsystems of treatments of which only part reach the conscious. According to Baddeley and Hitch (1974), this system of memory comprises a central administrator controlling other systems that are subordinate to it, the phonologic or articulatory loop—a mechanism of acoustic and linguistic treatment—and the visuo-spatial notebook. According to Norman and Sallice (1980), the central administrator is a supervisory attentional system coordinating and planning the treatments operating in the two systems that are subordinate to it. This model of working memory has modified the manner of investigating mechanisms of passage from short-term memory to long-term memory.

(d) *Long-term memory*

Long-term memory takes several forms that reveal different mechanisms and different cerebral structures and neuronal circuits. A memory is long-term when the information is conserved for a significant duration.

We can also ask: When is it short-term memory and when is it long-term memory? Two easily observed phenomena illustrate this distinction. This is the effect of primacy and the effect of recency: if a subject is given a list of words and is then asked to recite as many as possible from that list, he or she recalls the first words in the list (effect of primacy) and the last (effect of recency), while those in the middle of the list are forgotten. These two effects are interpreted as controlling, respectively, the putting of something into long-term memory and keeping it in short-term memory.

That said, the process of putting something into long-term memory "takes time": hours, months, years, as we will see later. Thus, recent facts that no longer come from working memory are not necessarily definitively memorized. This comes back to the question of the formation of memory, to which we will return. On the other hand, it may be that the trace of old facts that one has memorized will not be effaced, except in the case of destruction of the neuronal circuits, even if one may find it difficult to access these memories at a given moment.

The functioning of long-term memory can be described in three stages: memorizing or coding, conservation or retention, restoration or recall.

—Memorizing integrates information in multiple associative networks. In a way, it remains the content of the memory. It calls for several systems of coding: e.g., semantic, procedural, emotional context.

—Retention or conservation intervenes after formation of engrams. There is revision and consolidation of what is already memorized because of new experiences. The revisions suppose a recall to consciousness of what is already in memory, which consolidates the memory and explains the preservation of what is older (because recalled).

—Recall uses information stored in memory: it is a process that constantly intervenes in daily life (taking often the form of an involuntary memory) and underlies thought (like dreams). The voluntary evocation, distinct from recognition, can take the form of free recall or indexed recall.

5.1.2 Organization of Long-term Memory

The fact that all knowledge is not of the same nature has brought the authors to make several distinctions in the organization of long-term memory. Tulving and Schachter (1990) distinguished explicit memory from implicit memory, for what Squire (1987) designates under the terms *declarative memory* and *non-declarative memory*. Access to information stored in explicit memory is conscious, unlike access to information stored in implicit memory. These two systems are themselves divided into subsystems.

In the record of explicit memory, episodic memory is differentiated from semantic memory (Tulving, 1972). While semantic memory concerns knowledge of a general order, common to every one of us, episodic memory is based on personal history. These two forms will belong to different registers even if, sometimes, the circumstances in which one has learned certain information relevant to the register of semantic memory may have influenced the self-learning of this knowledge.

Implicit memory also takes several forms. Thus, procedural memory (that of gestures, skills) differs from conditioned responses just as it differs from the form of implicit memory discovered by psychologists thanks to paradigms of priming where a subject can more effectively and quickly treat information that has been linked to previous information, even if the previous information is not consciously remembered. In fact, it is the inaccessibility of memories to the consciousness that characterizes the various forms of implicit memory.

5.2 STRUCTURES AND CIRCUITS

5.2.1 The Papez Circuit

Discovered around 1930 by Papez, this circuit, bilateral and symmetrical, is located on the medial wall of the brain and links the cortex to the hypothalamus. Considered originally by Papez to be the circuit of emotion, this circuit was also called the *hippocampo-mamillo-thalamic circuit.* It corresponds to part of the connections that link the limbic structures to each other.

The information that they carry passes, in sequence, through the hippocampus, the mamillary bodies of the hypothalamus, the anterior nucleus of the thalamus, the cingular cortex, the entorhinal cortex and, finally, through the hippocampus again. It is thus a loop whose starting and end points are the hippocampus.

5.2.2 Middle Temporal Lobes, Memorization, Declarative Memory

The determining role of temporal lobes in declarative memory has been shown by the observation of the case of patients, experiments in animals, and experiments in functional imaging in humans.

Kluver and Bucy (1939) observed and described a behaviour that is quite curious in rats that have undergone a lobectomy of two temporal lobes. In their cage, where edible and inedible objects were placed, the rats showed classic exploratory behaviour, carrying objects to the mouth and eating the edible objects, but instead of turning away from the inedible objects, as rats conventionally do in such a situation, they continued to bring all the objects to their mouths (edible and inedible), as if they could not recognize them or had not learned that these objects were not edible.

In humans, it is primarily the study of a famous amnesic patient (referred to as HM) that made it possible to advance in the study of the role of temporal lobes in memory. Epileptic since the age of 10, HM underwent at about 30 years of age (in 1953) a bilateral middle temporal lobectomy to reduce his crises, which doctors had remarked often took place in this cerebral region. Following this operation, HM definitively lost his capacity to form new long-term memories (anterograde amnesia). Although he could remember a list of words that he repeated constantly (his short-term memory was thus intact), he forgot as soon as he was interrupted in his repetition. Moreover, he forgot events that occurred during the 3 years preceding his operation (retrograde amnesia): 20 months after his operation, he thought he was 27 although he was 29. On the other hand, his capacity to put things into procedural memory was intact.

The case of HM shows that the circuits of short-term memory and those of long-term memory differed, just like those of declarative memory and those of procedural memory. It shows also the role of temporal lobes in the consolidation of new information into declarative memory. It shows finally that the latter is long, since the memories of past years before the operation were lost in HM. At the time, doctors who operated on him estimated that they had destroyed 8 cm of cerebral tissue including all the hippocampus (or cornu ammonis, CA), the neighbouring cortex as well as the amygdala, but the longevity of HM and the advent of aMRI made it possible for them to assess, 30 years later, that only 5 cm of tissue was destroyed, leaving intact the posterior region of the hippocampi.

The post-mortem autopsy of another patient (RB) described by Zola-Morgan et al. (1986), also victim of anterograde amnesia (and retrograde for the period covering the 2 years preceding the cerebral vascular accident), but much less severe than that of HM, made it possible to observe in RB a specific bilateral lesion, limited to pyramidal cells of just the CA1 portion of the hippocampi.

The hippocampus (cornu ammonis) rests on the parahippocampic gyrus—the fifth temporal circumvolution—and is divided into three areas (CA1, CA2, CA3) that form a one-way loop, called trisynaptic loop. It receives afferences from associative sensory cortical areas, unimodal and multimodal, that carry highly elaborate information. This information, after having transited through the parahippocampic cortex, penetrates the hippocampus through the axons of the entorhinal cortex (see Fig. 5.1) and form synapse with the neurons of the dentate gyrus. This pathway of entry into the hippocampus is called the *perforant pathway.*

The entorhinal cortex is thus a centre of convergence of sensory information issuing from different associative areas of the neocortex. The information is then carried towards the pyramidal cells of the CA3 portion of the hippocampus and towards the CA1. The principal efferent pathway of the hippocampus leaves this at the level of the subiculum in the direction of the fornix, a thick network of fibres that end in the mamillary bodies of the hypothalamus. The mamillary bodies are in connection with the thalamus and with the cingulum, which sends information in return to the entorhinal cortex. This different pathway thus constitutes a loop that, with the amygdala, constitutes the essence of a limbic system. But this efferent pathway is not the only one. A second pathway is directed towards the contro-lateral

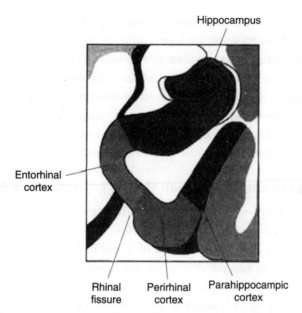

Fig. 5.1 The hippocampus and the adjacent cortex. Frontal section showing the different parts of the cortex of the middle temporal lobe (entorhinal, perirhinal, parahippocampic).

hippocampus. Finally, the hippocampus also sends information to associative cortical areas of the neocortex (sensory areas bu. also prefrontal and orbito-frontal cortex and cingulum). In conclusion, the hippocampus is a virtual square within which information is tried and treated ("worked", coded). Several experiments of cerebral imaging have confirmed this role of the hippocampus. An example is a PET experiment by Squire et al. (1992) showing activation of the hippocampus over the course of a task of memorization of words presented previously to the subjects in visual form. The data recorded by the authors on activations of the occipital cortex and of the prefrontal cortex in this same task support the hypothesis of a "visual cortex-hippocampus-prefrontal cortex" network for the memorization of written words (and thus of visual stimuli).

If one returns to the case of RB, the "sensory cortex-hippocampus-sensory cortex" circuit is interrupted at the CA1. The problems that follow show that this circuit is implicated in memorization, and that the hippocampus and the cortices that are adjacent play an essential role in the formation of explicit memory. The most recent research suggests even that it is the lesions of the perirhinal cortex that lead to the most severe problems.

We must remember that, despite their role in the process of memorizing, neither the hippocampus nor the nearby cortices are sites of long-term storage of explicit memory since the ablation of middle temporal lobes does not suppress episodic and semantic memories. It is likely that the memories are stored in other cortical regions. On the other hand, since in HM, as in RB, there is nevertheless a form of retrograde amnesia—limited to the months preceding the lesion—it is thought that the memories are stored temporarily in the cortex of the middle temporal lobe: the information subsists there during transformations essential to their consolidation before being stored over the long term in other cortical regions.

5.2.3 Hippocampus, Spatial Memory, Contextual Memory

If the hippocampus—and generally the middle temporal lobe—is not the site of permanent storage of explicit memories, it nevertheless seems that the right hippocampus is the site of storage of spatial memory. In fact, experiments carried out on rats placed in a maze (O'Keefe, 1979) have showed that when the rat moves, neurons that were till then silent begin to discharge when the rat reaches a particular place, while other neurons respond to another place. These neurons are called "place cells" and it thus seems that these place cells correspond to a mental map of the space.

In humans, PET experiments have been carried out on London taxi drivers to test the site of long-term storage of spatial memory: they were asked to simulate—using navigation sticks on a video game—a route in London, a city they know very well because of their profession. The regions that activated were the left caudal nucleus and the right hippocampus, which confirmed the preceding result obtained in the rat: the right hippocampus would be the site of storage of spatial memory. The activation of the caudate nucleus in this visual task of spatial navigation is attributed to the planning of movements in the navigation sticks to follow the route.

Some studies also suggest that the hippocampus and other structures of the middle temporal lobe play a role in contextual, episodic memory. This refers in the first place to "where" and "when", but not just these. It encompasses all that one can see and experience at the time at which one memorizes a particular item of information (e.g., an odour). This role has been suggested, notably, by experiments carried out on rats (Eichenbaum et al., 1988). The animal was trained to recognize two odours in a maze. The recording of the activity of populations of neurons showed that certain neurons identified as "place cells" during the spatial learning of the maze began to respond specifically to an odour during the learning (other neurons responding to the other odour).

The fact that some neurons could respond to the place or the odour or both stimuli is an argument in favour of the existence of a treatment of context by these neurons. After having observed that the ablation of hippocampi caused problems in this task of discriminating odours, the authors drew the hypothesis that memory of context could be due to neurons of the hippocampus.

5.2.4 Anterior Temporal Lobes and Long-term Memory

A profound retrograde amnesia extending over several decades was observed during lesions of the lateral cortex of the anterior temporal lobe (entorhinal cortex and perihippocampic cortex). This type of lesion was observed during encephalitis consecutive to a herpes virus attack on the brain and above all during degeneration of the brain as in Alzheimer's disease. Some patients injured in the anterior temporal lobe remained capable of forming new memories. The lesion is thus strictly limited to this region and this is called *isolated retrograde amnesia.*

This type of amnesia shows that the anterior part of the temporal lobe plays a role in the storage of old memories but not in the memorization of new information, which can be stored in places other than in the anterior temporal lobe. On the contrary, in the Alzheimer's patient who loses the capacity to form new memories as well as, gradually, old memories, the lesion extends progressively to the entire temporal pole—anterior and middle.

But the demonstration of the role of anterior temporal lobes in long-term memory does not exhaust the question of the long-term storage of memories. In fact, this is ultimately the form of memory for which there is less data about its storage sites. The reason for this is that, probably, the memories are generally stored in structures and neuronal networks implicated in the treatment of information that have forged memories, particularly in associative areas.

5.2.5 Diencephalus and Memorization

Within the diencephalus, three structures are strongly implicated in memorization: the anterior nuclei and dorsomedial of the thalamus as well as the mamillary bodies of the hypothalamus. Recall that one of the important efferent pathways of the hippocampus is the fornix, the axons of which project to the mamillary bodies, which themselves project to the anterior nucleus of the thalamus.

The Korsakoff syndrome was described in 1889 by the Russian doctor Korsakoff. It involves a severe problem of memory with fabrications and false recognitions in chronic alcoholic patients. The alcohol impedes the assimilation of vitamins (notably B1), which causes cerebral damage, particularly degeneration of the diencephalus—the dorsal medial nucleus of the thalamus and the mamillary bodies of the hypothalamus notably. Sometimes, the amnesia of a Korsakoff patient is called *diencephalic amnesia*. This syndrome combines an absolute anterograde amnesia and an extended retrograde amnesia. The anterograde amnesia is such that the patient cannot recall three words at the end of three minutes. Although the Korsakoff patient is reminiscent of HM and RB with respect to anterograde amnesia, unlike these two, he or she is affected with profound retrograde amnesia, does not seem conscious of the problem, displays numerous false recognitions, and, above all, has no lesion of the middle temporal region. This region cannot thus be held solely responsible for the formation of explicit memories.

Some ischaemic lesions of the thalamus also manifest as a severe anterograde amnesia and a retrograde amnesia of variable intensity. The patient is anosognosic and presents fabrications. The essence of the problem lies in acquisition and coding. In certain cases, the patient may display problems in temporal ordering of memories, their duration, the time that has passed since, and so on (this is called *chronotaxis*). It is the lesion of the right dorso-medial nucleus of the thalamus that seems responsible for this trouble with time: it involves the capacity of the right hemisphere to form a spatial representation of time.

Moreover, thalamic haemorrhages for the left lesions cause a deficiency in verbal memory and for the right lesions a deficiency in visual memory with fabrications about places and persons in the familiar surroundings of the patient.

5.2.6 The Amygdalian Circuit of Emotions

Another component of the limbic system, apart from the Papez circuit, is the amygdalo-thalamo-cingular circuit, which receives information from the hypothalamus, the cerebral trunk, and the hippocampus. The amygdala is made up of a nucleus located at the anterior end of the hippocampus. Its afferences come from the parahippocampic gyrus and hippocampus, while its efferences are targeted toward the hypothalamus and the dorso-medial nucleus of the thalamus. It is also integrated within the network that links the central grey nuclei of the frontal lobe. The amygdalo-thalamo-cingular circuit is thus connected to the Papez circuit. Even if it is not a memory circuit, properly speaking, it nevertheless intervenes in memorization in giving an emotional connotation to information to be memorized.

5.2.7 Basal Ganglia, Procedural Memory

The basal ganglia constitute one of the regions essential to the regulation of voluntary movements. At the interface between the sensory cortex and the premotor cortex, they ensure the "link" between sensoriality and motivity and are at the basis of sensory-motor learning. This is a "primitive" form of memory, that of skills, sensory-motors that allow us to react to the solicitations of the environment. The term "primitive" refers to the anteriority of the appearance of the underlying circuits in phylogenetic evolution and the ontogenetic development of the brain. It is interesting to note that in the Alzheimer's patient, this memory remains intact for a very long time when other forms of memory, and more generally the cognitive functions, have disappeared. This is why, for example, these patients, faced with a closed door, automatically turn the handle and leave the room. Alzheimer's disease is a cerebral degeneration of the cortex. The deep circuits passing through the basal ganglia are thus affected later.

A PET experiment (Grafton et al., 1995) confirms the role of the motor-cortico-subcortical loop in the implicit learning of motor sequences. The authors compared cerebral activation during a simple task of explicit motor learning of pressing buttons in response to sequences of stimuli and during a task of implicit motor learning. In the latter, the subject must achieve the same task as before but with a second task to be done: to count low-frequency sounds among a set of sounds of different frequencies. This task of counting is designed to prevent the explicit character of the motor learning. The authors observed that the two conditions of learning of the motor sequence (explicit and implicit) activate the motor cortex and the putamen (one of the basal ganglia), other regions being specifically activated by the particular conditions of the task (simple or double).

Within these central grey nuclei, it seems that the striatum—the caudate and putamen together—receiving the afferences of the frontal and parietal cortices and projecting to the thalamic nuclei and the motor cortex plays a key role in learning of motor skills and, more generally, in procedural memory. An experiment by Knowlton et al. (1996) on amnesiac patients and Parkinsonian patients made it possible to demonstrate this. The authors subjected the patients to a task calling for declarative (semantic) memory and to a task of procedural memory. The latter proceeded in the following manner: combinations of charts (1, 2 or 3 among 4 possible maps) comprising geometric figures were presented to the subject. Then, the experimenter decided that each combination was associated with good weather or bad weather, according to a certain probability. The subjects had to then learn to predict the weather as a function of the combination that was presented to them. For each trial, the subjects were informed about their performance (good prediction, bad prediction). The amnesic patients—who had bilateral lesions of the hippocampus or of the diencephalus) succeeded in this second task of procedural memory as well as the control subjects while they failed at the task of declarative memory. The performances of Parkinsonian patients were strictly opposite to those of the amnesiacs: they succeeded at the task of declarative memory and failed at the task of procedural memory. Recall that Parkinson's disease consists of a degeneration of dopaminergic neurons of the black matter that projects to the striatum. The attack of the striatum that follows from the absence of its dopaminergic afferences leads thus not only to characteristic motor problems (trembling, difficulty in initiating movement, postural rigidity) but also to difficulties in learning procedures other than motor skills.

Thus, the basal ganglia are implicated in the memory of procedures, whether or not they act on gestures and motor sequences.

5.2.8 Frontal Lobe and Working Memory

Within the frontal lobe, the prefrontal part is the most developed in humans and it is known generally that it plays an essential role in executive functions. Nevertheless, the detail of its functioning is poorly understood. Since the introduction of the Baddeley model of working memory, the dorso-lateral part of this region is considered by researchers to be susceptible of playing a pivotal role in this form of memory—particularly what Baddeley called the "central administrator"—because of its numerous interconnections with the structures of the temporal lobe and the diencephalus.

Among the numerous studies on the question, the fMRI study of Courtney et al. (1997) is the primary one to be cited. These authors set a task of maintaining working memory of specific visual stimuli, photos of faces, these stimuli being presented randomly among a set of non-specific stimuli. These non-specific stimuli were "scrambled", made up of faces cut into small portions and mixed (the digitization of images made this an easy operation). This procedure made available images that were in both cases (faces and scrambled images) made up of strictly identical physical characteristics. Thus, the authors were able to distinguish regions activated by mnesic treatment from those activated by purely perceptive treatment (Fig. 5.2).

—When the images are scrambled, essentially the regions of the ventral visual pathway are activated: the posterior portions of the lingual gyrus and the fusiform gyrus as well as the inferior occipital sulcus.

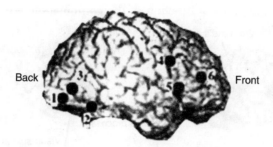

Fig. 5.2 Activation of frontal lobe during a task of maintaining working memory (Courtney et al., 1997): an fMRI study. The stimuli presented were faces or "scrambled" images constituted of the same faces in which the pixels were mixed. The presentation of images activates the regions of the ventral visual pathway (1, 2, 3). The maintenance of working memory of faces also activates the frontal lobe (4, 5, 6). 1, posterior part of lingual and fusiform gyri; 2, anterior portion of fusiform gyrus; 3, inferior occipital sulcus; 4, inferior frontal gyrus, anterior portion; 5, inferior frontal gyrus and anterior insula; 6, inferior frontal gyrus, middle portion.

—During the presentation of the faces and the activation of the fusiform gyrus and inferior occipital sulcus (regions of treatment of faces), it is the anterior and middle portions of the superior frontal gyri that are the most active.

—Finally, during the task of memorization of faces it is the frontal regions that are the most active: the inferior frontal gyrus, the anterior insula and the anterior part of the middle frontal gyrus.

These data from functional imaging in humans are entirely consistent with the observations of Goldman-Rakic (summarized in an article in *Pour la Science* in 1992) in the ape, thanks to the recording of cortical neurons. It nevertheless is useful to specify that although some authors suggest that the prefrontal region is only one place in which the actions of slave systems (phonologic loop and visuo-spatial notebook) are coordinated (central administrator), others, such as Goldman-Rakic (1997), find this region of the prefrontal cortex (Brodmann area 46) to be a virtual temporary storage of information necessary to the task at hand.

That being so, demonstration of the role of the prefrontal cortex does not exhaust the question of all the structures underlying the functioning of the working memory. In Fig. 5.3 are shown the regions implicating on the one hand the phonological loop and on the other hand the visuo-spatial notebook in the Baddeley model of working memory.

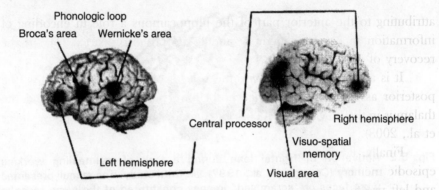

Fig. 5.3 The cerebral regions corresponding to the Baddeley model of working memory (www.lecerveau.mcgill.ca). The phonological loop activates the areas implicated in language (left hemisphere). The visuo-spatial memory ("visuo-spatial notebook") activates the visual areas of the right hemisphere. The frontal activation of the two hemispheres corresponds to the implementation of a central processor.

5.2.9 Models of Coding and Recuperation: Hemispheric Asymmetry

The Tulving research team (Kapur et al., 1994) elaborated, on the basis of PET experiments, a fundamental model (HERA or hemispheric encoding retrieval asymmetry) of cerebral functioning in the processes of coding and recovery of information in memory. According to this model, coding into episodic memory is the result of the activity of the left prefrontal cortex, while the recovery of the episodic information is the result of the activity of the right prefrontal cortex. Data acquired subsequently enriched and refined the HERA model. It should also be noted that the left prefrontal cortex is also implicated in the recovery of information in semantic memory, which suggests a specific role of the left prefrontal cortex in the recovery of verbal information. For example, the HERA model will be applied certainly to verbal material but the coding of non-verbal material could implicate the right prefrontal cortex (for review, see Desgranges et al., 2003).

Other models have been elaborated. In the CARA (cortical asymmetry of reflective activity) model of Nolde et al. (1998), the right prefrontal cortex intervenes only in recovery for simple tasks, while it is the two prefrontal cortices that intervene in recall for complex tasks. The retrieval mode (REMO) of Lepage et al. (2000) lists the sites associated with the mode of recovery in episodic memory: these sites notably include the anterior cingular cortex and different right frontal regions. The HIPER (hippocampus encoding retrieval) model of Lepage et al. (1998) complements HERA in attributing to the anterior part of the hippocampus a role in encoding of information in episodic memory and to its posterior part a role in the recovery of such information.

It is also appropriate to cite the role of other structures such as the posterior associative cortex, the cerebellum, the cingular cortex, and the thalamus in the functioning of episodic memory (for review, see Desgranges et al., 2003).

Finally, it is a vast network that is implicated in the functioning of episodic memory, a network within which the hippocampus and the right and left prefrontal cortex play important but distinct roles. Two networks underlie episodic memory and semantic memory: a bilateral network for episodic memory and a left network for semantic memory. These networks are common for some parts (the left prefrontal cortex, the left temporo-parietal cortex, the cingular cortex, the right cerebellum, the thalamus), while the right prefrontal cortex, the hippocampus, the posterior cingular cortex, and the precuneus are specifically implicated in episodic memory (Cabezza and Nyburg, 2000). This tends to show that the systems of episodic memory and semantic memory are not totally autonomous or totally independent.

Thus, one can integrate the **HERA**, **CARA** and **HIPER** models as follows:

—The left prefrontal cortex is implicated in coding in episodic memory; it is also implicated in the recovery of semantic memory, but only in complex tasks.

—The right prefrontal cortex is implicated in recovery in episodic memory (simple and complex tasks).

—The anterior hippocampus is implicated in coding in episodic memory.

—The posterior hippocampus is implicated in recovery in episodic memory.

There is thus a complementarity of right and left prefrontal cortices and the anterior and posterior hippocampus.

5.3 THE CELLULAR BASIS OF MEMORY

5.3.1 Potentialization over the Long Term

Ramón y Cajal was the first, in 1894, to advance the idea that learning could facilitate the development and growth of synapses (called "protuberances" at the time) and thus to open the avenue to the concept of cerebral plasticity.

Subsequently, Hebb (1949) put forth the hypothesis that the activity of neurons put into play during the course of a task of learning could persist for some time, like clearing a path, opening a pathway of nature to facilitate, subsequently, the activation of this population of neurons. More precisely, according to him, the simultaneous activation of a population of neurons could modify in the long term their connections and synapses and it is the long-term modifications that constitute the cellular bases of memory. After the demonstration of modifications of synapses after habituation in the mollusc, Bliss and Lomo (1973) described, in rabbit, a phenomenon of synaptic modification. A high-frequency stimulation, which leads to a high-frequency action potential of a neuronal pathway running from the sensory cortex to the hippocampus (in other terms the perforant pathway described earlier), induces a significant and durable increase in the efficacy of the synaptic transmission at this level. The target neurons of the hippocampus, thus stimulated, subsequently have a diminished threshold of excitation, that is, they respond to a stimulation that previously was too low to trigger an electric response on their part. This phenomenon has for long been called *long-term potentialization* (LTP).

It has been demonstrated that LTP was a phenomenon characteristic of the neurons of the perforant pathway as well as some associative areas, and it is certainly one of the essential supports of memory.

5.3.2 Molecular Mechanisms of LTP or Synaptic Plasticity

The synapses modifiable by LTP use glutamate as neurotransmitter. Recall that it is an excitatory neurotransmitter, widespread in neurons of the hippocampus but also in most of the cortical regions and in numerous subcortical regions. In particular, it is the excitatory neurotransmitter highly frequent in the sensory pathways.

Thus, during an excitation, glutamate is liberated by the presynaptic neuron. At the post-synaptic neuron level, there are receptors of neurotransmitters as follows, for glutamate: AMPA (alpha-amino-3-hydroxy-5-methyl-4-isoxazole) and NMDA (N-methyl-d-aspartate). While the AMPA receptor is coupled with an ionic column causing the entry of sodium in the post-synaptic neuron, the NMDA receptor is coupled with an ionic canal allowing the entry of calcium.

The AMPA is active when the situation is normal. The NMDA receptor is thus inactive. In fact, the calcic canal of the NMDA receptor is thus blocked by magnesium ions. On the other hand, when the message transmitted by the presynaptic neuron is high (high frequency of AP), the quantity of glutamate liberated in the synaptic pore is high and there is a significant depolarization of the post-synaptic membrane. It is here that the NDMA enters into play. The magnesium ions retire and release the ionic canal. The NMDA receptor thus undergoes a deformation that has the effect of opening the ionic canal and the calcium ions enter massively into the post-synaptic neuron. This triggers a series of molecular reactions that are manifested in long-term modification of the synapse, remodelling of neuronal circuits, change in the form and size of synapses, insertion of receptors of glutamate with transformation of silencing synapses into active synapses, and growth of new synapses.

LANGUAGE 95

6

Language

Systems of communication exist in all animal species, but only humans are endowed with speech and language. The fundamental difference between systems of communication in animals and human language pertains to the limited and non-productive character of animal communication, while human language is creative and practically unlimited. Humans unceasingly produce, create, different combinations of words according to grammatical rules while the most evolved animals can only reproduce simple codes of which they have been taught the significance. Although some believe, in the present state of research, that we will be able to demonstrate one day that some animals among the most evolved—certain apes or dolphins—are endowed with a form of thought and language, we must observe that that has so far not been demonstrated. Experiments carried out in apes that have been taught sign language[1] show that what could belong to linguistic production (combining words to express a thought) does not go beyond an association of two words. On the contrary, human language uses sounds, symbols, and gestures. Moreover, the signs of language are organized according to a syntax proper to each language or dialect.

---

[1] Since no animal has a larynx that allows it to reproduce the sounds of human language, sign language is most suitable for these experiments.

There is no doubt that it is the spectacular development of the human brain and more particularly of its neo-cortex—in relation to that of other species—and the complexity of its organization that "makes the difference" and allows the human being to produce and understand language.

In this chapter, we succinctly recall the theoretic framework of models of treatment of language before addressing the cerebral anatomo-functional organization of human language.

6.1 THEORETICAL CONTEXT

To be understood, the words we perceive must be treated to give them meaning, beyond the simple recognition of acoustic or visual signals emitted by the sounds of the speech or the visual characters of the words and phrases we read. For linguists, language is structured at several levels: (1) phonological, that of elementary units—phonemes—of oral language; (2) lexical (words); (3) syntactic (the combination of words into phrases); (4) semantic (the meaning of words); (5) pragmatic (use of words). Taken one by one, these levels are themselves the objects of different concepts. For example, the organization of vocabulary itself is always debatable: is it a list of words (the oldest concept) or a set organized into a system or a reconstruction? The various prevailing conceptions lead notably to another debate, that which opposes the modularist conception (by reference to Fodor, 1983) to connectionist models. According to the modularist approach (Forster, 1979), language is treated in three distinct steps, realized by subsystems specializing in the treatment of language (subsystems of phonological treatment, lexical treatment, and syntactical treatment). These steps rapidly link up, automatically and without the need for conscious thought: a sequence of letters immediately suggests a word, a sequence of words immediately suggests a phrase. One often associates this conception to the serial model of treatment of information in which each operation begins only when the preceding one has been completed (phonological treatment before lexical treatment, etc.) even if, as noted by Segui (1998), the serial model is not one presupposed to be necessary to modular organization. The connectionist models (Marlsen-Wilson, 1984) range from total negation of the concept of levels of treatment to more nuanced positions in which the levels exist but interact: thus, for example, the processes of treatment of syntactic organization of the phrase call for lexical information (which flows from the modularist conception and a model of serial treatment) but also for information of semantic, pragmatic nature. This organization, which supposes interactions and exchanges of information between the different levels, is that of the "cascade" model of McClelland (1979) or "cohort" model of Marlsen-Wilson (1984). Most of the models proposed at present combine these two conceptions, the modular approach being preferred for the primary processes of treatment (processes of identification), the interactive approach being proposed for the rest of the treatment (processes of interpretation).

But the comprehension of language is not the only question that must be treated. In fact, it is useful to distinguish not only the processes of language comprehension from processes of language production, but also the processes of treatment of written language from those of oral language.

Specialists in neuropsychology and cognitive neuroscience, particularly those who use methods of brain imaging, are obviously directly involved in the question. The question posed to them is, in fact, whether one can identify brain structures, neuronal networks, the activity of which is concomitant with the different operations of language treatment, and whether one can refine the reciprocal organization of the coming into play of these various structures.

6.2   THE FIRST DISCOVERY OF AREAS OF LANGUAGE AND APHASIA

It was obviously Broca and Wernicke who first, and from the mid-19th century, helped to highlight the revelation of the dissociation between production and comprehension of oral language. In 1861, Broca (a neurosurgeon), first related a lesion of the frontal lobe—the left inferior frontal gyrus—of one of his patients (M. Leborgne) with the incapacity of this patient to speak, except to pronounce one syllable, "Tan", two times or more in succession (Tan Tan Tan ...).[2] Having subsequently observed other patients with the same type of problem, he deduced from this that the third convolution of the left frontal lobe was the site of the "faculty of articulated language". Through these studies, Broca thus immediately highlighted a cerebral region of production of oral language—today called *Broca's area*—and the lateralization of this area, the functional asymmetry of the two cerebral hemispheres. Some years later (in 1870), Wernicke, a German neurologist, having autopsied the brain of one of his patients, highlighted another area of language located, this time, in the posterior regions of the left superior temporal gyrus. But the lesion of this patient was associated with an entirely different type of problem. Unlike "Tan Tan", this patient had a significant verbal deficiency but his language was a combination of sounds, words, and phrases without meaning. The region

---

[2] Hence the name Tan Tan given to this patient in the literature.

affected being close to the auditory area, Wernicke deduced that the area he discovered—since called *Wernicke's area*—was a site for auditory storage of words. Wernicke thus set forth the hypothesis of a sensori-motor network between the area that he had discovered, believed to be the site of a "sensory memory of words" and Broca's area, thought to be the site of a "motor memory of words".

Their works thus allowed us to distinguish two forms of aphasia, named after Broca and Wernicke. The study of numerous other patients has long led to the refinement of the semiology of these aphasias and to the highlighting of other dissociations and types of aphasia (for a detailed description, see Sieroff, 2004). But all the authors are not in agreement on the anatomical delimitation of these areas.

6.2.1 Broca's Aphasia

Broca was able to associate the aphasia of his patient Tan Tan to the lesion of the third left frontal convolution—or left inferior frontal gyrus. It is now known that, anatomically, the Broca's area thus highlighted comprises three parts, corresponding to the areas 44, 45 and 47 of Brodmann (see Fig. 6.1),

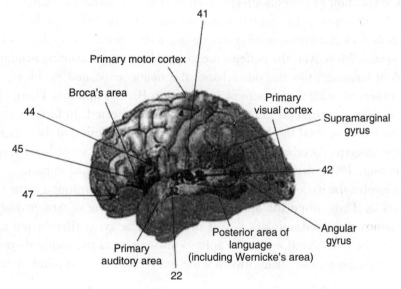

Fig. 6.1 Areas of language. Broca's area corresponds to the left inferior frontal gyrus (third convolution) comprising the areas of Brodmann 44 (posterior part of the opercle or operculus), 45 (triangular part or pars triangularis), 47 (inferior or orbitary part) as well as the left insula (at the basis of the Sylvian fissure) and the subcortical white matter of these regions. Wernicke's area comprises the superior temporal gyrus (areas 22, 41, 42 of Brodmann) and the adjacent parietal regions (angular gyrus).

that is, respectively: the posterior part (or pars opercularis), the middle or triangular part (or pars triangularis), and the inferior or orbitary part (pars orbitaris). Some authors also include in Broca's area the anterior insula and the subcortical white matter.

Conventionally, Broca's aphasia is associated with non-fluent elocution, but this problem is often associated with anomia (incapacity to name persons or objects). Also, sometimes the problems are not limited to speech: the patients thus also have difficulty reading or writing. It seems nevertheless that their comprehension of language is generally intact. Let us add that Broca's aphasia is often associated with a right hemiplegia, that is, a paralysis of the right side of the brain. In fact, the severity of problems depends on the amplitude of the lesion, the region affected, and the circuits thus interrupted between this region of the brain and others. Thus, the problems observed in Broca's aphasia can be more or less severe, and the study of lesions that cause it gradually allows refinement of networks and regions implicated in the production of language.

6.2.2 Wernicke's Aphasia

The verbal flow of patients affected with Wernicke's aphasia is highly fluent, but their discourse is incomprehensible because it is studded with substitutions of phonemes and words, neologisms, despite a structure that overall preserves the syntax. Moreover, the patients are incapable of understanding written or spoken language. On the other hand, the major associated problems are not observed, such as the hemiplegia found in Broca's aphasia. There also, the severity of problems depends on the regions affected. In fact, although the patient described by Wernicke was the carrier of a lesion of the superior temporal gyrus (Brodmann areas 22, 41, and 42), it has since been shown (Damasio, 1995) that the lesion implicated in this form of aphasia could also involve the parietal regions adjacent to the superior temporal gyrus (see Fig. 6.1). Thus, when the aphasia involves only reading of written words, the lesion that predominates is that of the angular gyrus (Brodmann area 39); on the other hand, when the aphasia also concerns the comprehension of oral language, the attack involves the entire superior temporal gyrus.

6.2.3 Other Types of Aphasia

Since the discoveries of Broca and Wernicke, not only the knowledge of aphasia named after them, but also the existence of other forms of aphasia has been demonstrated. Without mentioning them all (see Sieroff, 2004), we can cite conduction aphasia, which seems to be due to a lesion of fibres of the arcuate bundle linking the areas of Broca and Wernicke as well as the angular gyrus. The two areas are intact but they become disconnected. This type of aphasia affects neither verbal fluency nor comprehension, which remains good, but it manifests itself in paraphasia, transformations and omissions of words, difficulties of repetition and denomination, which indicates the fact that it is the communication between the areas of Broca and Wernicke that is affected. In global aphasia, the deficiencies involve thus comprehension and verbal fluency as well as the problems encountered in conduction aphasia. The lesion is thus extended to the whole of the areas of Broca and Wernicke, as well as to the arcuate bundle.

6.3 INPUT OF THE SPLIT-BRAIN MODEL

In animals, many studies designed to refine the respective roles of the right and left hemispheres have been achieved by sectioning the callous bodies. This "split-brain" method has been used by Gazzaniga's team to the extent that the section of the callous body has been applied to therapeutic ends in epileptic patients. Gazzaniga thus realized a series of experiments to astonishing effect by presenting different images in left and right visual fields that were transmitted to a single hemisphere (respectively left and right) since the section of the callous body prohibited transmission of what reached one hemisphere to the other hemisphere. To achieve this type of experiment with success, the images must be projected very rapidly to avoid displacements of sight that will allow the same eye (and thus the same hemisphere) to treat right and left images. Of course, the subject must look "straight ahead" in order for the images to be effectively projected in the monocular visual fields. The images, phrases, and words projected in the right visual field, and thus treated by the left hemisphere, are perfectly described and named by the patient. If one places an object in his right hand, he describes it verbally without difficulty. On the other hand, he fails at these tests when the images are projected in his left visual field (treated by the right hemisphere). Similarly, he cannot verbally describe an object placed in his left hand.

The studies based on this principle have shown that the right hemisphere is nevertheless capable of treating certain linguistic information. Faced with a word presented on the right hemisphere, the patient is not capable of reading it aloud. Still, when presented with cards representing various objects including the one that corresponds to this word, the patient chooses the right card. This suggests obviously that the right hemisphere is capable of treating words even if it is not capable of pronouncing them. Chiarello (1991) has even shown that this capacity concerns particularly the words linked semantically. Thus, the right hemisphere is capable of treating aspects of language that are particularly important since they are related to meaning.

These observations lead to distinction of various aspects of language such as comprehension and production, of course, but also semantic and syntactic aspects, in written as well as oral language.

6.4 THE MENTAL VOCABULARY

The existence of a mental vocabulary or a form of mental representation of words hardly seems to be a matter of doubt. The organization of this mental vocabulary does not correspond exactly to that of a dictionary. The meaning of words (semantic) probably plays an essential role in the storage of words. This is in any case what emerges from various experiments, current in psychology, consisting of asking subjects to decide as quickly and precisely as possible whether the stimuli that are presented to them (successively) are words or non-words. When this type of task is realized by applying a bait paradigm (before each stimulus a word is presented), it seems that not only is the lexical decision faster for the words, but it is even more so (and more exact) when the stimulus-word is linked semantically to the preceding word (for example, if the word "dog" is the bait, the lexical decision will be faster if the stimulus is the word "cat" than if the word is "table"). Similarly, if a bait word is presented and then a word that the subject must pronounce, the response is faster than if the bait and the stimulus are linked semantically. This works towards a mental representation of the meaning of words. The nature of this association remains debatable: is it a semantic network, as suggested by Collins and Loftus (1975), or is it a vaster conceptual network outside the mental vocabulary?

The study of various pathologies suggests some idea of the organization of this vocabulary. We know semantic paraphasies (with the use of one word in place of another that is linked to it semantically: e.g., "cat" in place of "dog") or the denomination of the category (e.g., "animals") in place of the denomination of the object (e.g., "cat"). Moreover, these problems may concern only one category of object.

In a PET experiment, Damasio et al. (1996) studied brain-damaged patients showing problems with naming of objects, comparing them with healthy subjects. The authors demonstrated the following:

—The anterior portion of the left infero-temporal cortex (ITC or temporal pole) was associated with problems of denomination of category of persons.

—The middle portion of the left ITC was associated with problems of the naming of category of animals.

—The posterior portion of the ITC as well as the left temporo-parieto-occipital junction was associated with problems of the naming of category of tools.

These problems in naming do not prevent patients from describing the objects, which shows that they recognize them. Moreover, the naming of these various categories of visual objects in healthy subjects also activates other brain regions, which differ according to the category of visual objects. For example, the naming of tools is accompanied by an activation of ITC and the left temporo-parieto-occipital junction as well as the left premotor area. This left premotor area is also activated when subjects are asked to imagine the movements of handling a tool.

On the basis of these results, Damasio et al. (1996) concluded not only the existence of a mental vocabulary but also its organization in three levels implicating different cerebral regions: a conceptual level containing semantic information, a lexical level comprising the words themselves, and a phonological level corresponding to the sound of words. While the lexical level seems to concern only the left hemisphere, the semantic network is supported by both hemispheres.

6.5 COMPREHENSION OF LANGUAGE

The comprehension of language in the first place supposes the perceptive analysis of inputs, obviously different according to whether it is oral language (auditory inputs) or written language (visual inputs). An essential difference concerns the segmentation of inputs: the written language comprises words separated by spaces, phrases separated by punctuation, and so on. Here there are indications essential for a first step in the comprehension of written language. These indications do not exist in the oral language. On the other hand, the oral language is accompanied by prosodic information (rhythm and intonation), which introduces a type of segmentation other than what the language describes. This is the reason it is so important, when one reads out loud, to read with expression.

6.5.1 Perceptive Analysis

The inputs of written language and those of oral language are very different. The acts of seeing words and hearing words do not activate the same regions (see Fig. 6.2), as shown by Petersen and Fiez (1993) in a PET experiment.

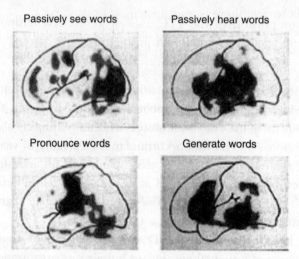

Fig. 6.2 Regions activated by language (Petersen and Fiez, 1993). PET experiment in which the subject must passively listen to or see words (above), pronounce or generate words (below). The upper pat of the figure shows the activation of sensory areas corresponding to sensory inputs of oral language (hearing) or written language (vision).

For written language, the problem that the reader first faces, at this perceptive stage, is to translate the visual stimuli (lines, traits, curves) into letters and then to assemble these into words. Of course, this supposes maintenance of visual stimuli in iconic memory, which is necessary for such assembling.

Little is known of the manner in which the brain proceeds to recognize letters. On the other hand, a PET study by Petersen et al. (1990) made it possible to show that recognition of the form of letters and words activates the left extra-striate occipital cortex. More precisely, words and pseudo-words responding to rules of assembly of letters in the English language (which was the language of the subjects of the experiment) activated similar regions. On the other hand, these regions were not activated by combinations of letters not resembling words or by false letters made up of forms more or less resembling letters. Moreover, in the case of words (not in the case of pseudo-words), the left frontal cortex was also activated. The authors interpreted these results as displaying a perceptive treatment of high level within the extra-striate occipital cortex and of a semantic treatment of words within the frontal cortex. Note that these data conform with those of the neuropsychology relative to patients who have a lesion of the left occipital extra-striate cortex displaying pure alexia.

For oral language, there is transformation of an acoustic signal into an abstract representation. Petersen and Fiez (1993) showed that the hearing of words activates the left temporo-parietal region and the anterior portion of the superior temporal gyrus (STG). The temporo-parietal cortex comprises the angular gyrus (Brodmann area 39) and the supramarginal gyrus (Brodmann area 40). The combination of these results and those drawn from the study of brain-damaged patients suggests that the temporo-parietal region could ensure the phonological coding of oral language, that is, to generate representations of the sound type.

6.5.2   Syntactic Analysis and Semantic Analysis: The Input of EP

After the analysis of sensory entries, the system of comprehension of language must ensure access to the meaning of words and to the analysis of structural relationships between these words. Numerous EP studies (and more recently MEG studies) have made it possible to refine the organization of phonological, semantic and syntactic treatments.

(a) *Semantic treatment and the N4 effect*

We have already mentioned in Chapter 3 the N400 wave, discovered by Kutas and Hillyard (1980). The authors presented to the subjects phrases in which the last word could be more or less incongruous in relation to the context of the phrase: for example, (1) I drink my coffee with milk and *sugar* (semantically correct phrase), (2) I drink my coffee with milk and a *dog* (the word "dog" is incongruous in the semantic context of the phrase); (3) I drink my coffee with milk and *salt* (the word "salt" is also incongruous but belongs to the semantic category of foods). Kutas and Hillyard (1980) showed that, 400 ms after the words "dog" and "salt", a negative wave developed at the surface of the scalp, in the centro-parietal region. This N400 was more ample when the semantic incongruity was strong. In our example, the word "dog" caused a more ample N400 than the word "salt", while the word "sugar" did not cause N400. This effect was called the "N4 effect". Having varied the types of incongruity (e.g., a word written in capital letters while the rest of the phrase was written in lower case), as well as the types of presentation (oral or visual), these researchers and others showed that only semantic incongruity caused an N400 and this was true no matter what the modality of presentation of the phrase (auditory or visual). Although we have already mentioned the existence of an N400 when an incongruity is introduced in a known face (Jemel et al., 1996), the effect seems nevertheless highly specific of semantic treatment, that is, of the analysis of meaning (of the phrase with respect to the language). Furthermore, the N400 observed in the incongruity within a face does not occur in the same cerebral regions as the N400 typical of language. One group of researchers (Patel et al., 1998) looking to observe an N400 in introducing an incongruity in a "musical phrase" by introducing a discordant note at the end of a known melody observed only a P600, showing by the same the specificity of the semantic in the matter of language.

(b) *Treatment of syntax*

Here also, specific waves have been observed on the EP. Two waves mark the syntactic processes (for review see Friederici, 2002): one early negativity (between 150 and 500 ms after a violation of syntax) observed on the left anterior part of the scalp, and a late positivity (600 to 1000 ms after the syntactic violation) observed in the centro-parietal region. This last (P600), the most commonly studied, was observed for different types of syntactic violation but it is greater when the violation pertains to the order of words (e.g., the small boy eats green apple *the*) than when it pertains to a violation of subject-verb agreement (e.g., the children *eats* a green apple). Taking into account the latency of these waves, the first wave marks automatic processes of syntactic treatment while the P600 marks controlled processes of reanalysis of syntax. It must be noted that in some cases of syntactic violations, the P600 is preceded by an N400, probably because in this case the syntactic violation is such that it distorts the meaning of the phrase.

(c) *Chronometry of syntactic and semantic processes*

The temporal dynamics of various waves observed (early negativity, N400, P600) suggests that, at least for certain phrases difficult to understand, the semantic analysis (marked by N400) could be inserted in automatic processes (marked by early negativity) and the controlled processes (marked by P600) of syntactic analysis. Nevertheless, the authors do not retain a sequential (serial) organization of these steps of treatment and lean rather toward a "cascade" model in which some of these processes of treatment occur in parallel.

6.5.3 Localization of Syntactic and Semantic Processes

Following their PET experiments, the team of Petersen (1990, 1993) proposed a model in which, besides the superior temporal gyrus implicated in the phonological coding, the supramarginal gyrus and the angular gyrus, multimodal associative areas, will be at the interface between conceptual, articulatory and semantic systems: the supramarginal gyrus ensures the passage of conceptual treatment from vocabulary to the articulatory system; the left and right angular gyri will be implicated in the semantic treatment (in relation with the posterior cingular gyrus).

Nevertheless, the existence of syntactic and semantic processes occurring partly in parallel, as shown by Friederici (2002) from EP studies, made it possible to go further in the localization of these processes. This author in effect sought to identify the cerebral generators of waves marking the syntactic and semantic processes. For N400 (semantic analysis), several generators have been found: in temporo-medial structures close to the hippocampus, in areas located along the superior temporal groove, in the left temporal lobe, in regions close to the left auditory cortex (in the case of oral language). Generators of early negative component marking the syntactic analysis have been found in the two hemispheres, with a predominance in the left hemisphere, at the inferior frontal and anterior temporal level. Finally, the results relative to generators of P600 are too disparate to be mentioned. At most, one can mention that in patients brain-damaged at the level of basal ganglia and in Parkinsonian patients, P600 marking the syntactic processes is absent (or of very small amplitude), while these same patients do not present the anomaly of early negativity, which suggests an important role of the basal ganglia in the generation of this P600 and thus in the controlled processes of syntax treatment.

fMRI studies complemented these results in EP. For example, Friederici et al. (2000) asked their subjects to listen to phrases varying in the presence or absence of syntactic information (normal phrases, phrases violating the syntax with pseudo-words, lists of words and pseudo-words that lacked semantic or syntactic information). Curiously, all the situations activated the left and right frontal lobes with the exception of listening to normal phrases, which led the authors to advance the idea that, in this case, the phrases are treated automatically when they are being understood. Besides, listening to phrases in which the syntax is violated activates the temporal planum in the two hemispheres and the deep part of the left frontal opercle. The authors concluded that the treatment of syntax could implicate the two temporal cortices and the left frontal lobe. Then, the same team (Friederici et al., 2003) took up again the principle of the preceding experiment by adding a condition of listening to phrases that were semantically incorrect. In these conditions (see Fig. 6.3), listening to two types of incorrect phrases activates the superior temporal gyrus but (1) listening to phrases with syntactic violation activates the posterior part of the left superior temporal gyrus, the left posterior frontal opercle as well as the putamen; (2) listening to phrases with semantic violation activates the middle portion of the superior temporal

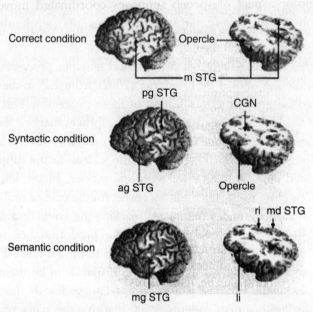

Fig. 6.3 Cerebral activations corresponding to syntactic and semantic treatment (Friederici et al., 2003). iMRF experiment in which the subject hears normal phrases (above), phrases comprising a violation of syntax (middle) or phrases comprising a semantic violation (below). Left: left cerebral hemisphere. Right: horizontal section showing activations in the two hemispheres. Hearing correct phrases activates the left opercle as well as the middle part of the right and left superior temporal gyrus (m STG). Hearing phrases containing a syntactic violation activates anterior and posterior portions of the left temporal gyrus (respectively ag STG and pg STG) as well as the left opercle and the central grey cells (CGN). Hearing phrases containing a semantic violation activates the middle portion of the left and right superior temporal gyrus (mg STG and md STG), the left insula (li) and the right insula (ri).

gyrus, the insula, in the two hemispheres. Note that in no case is the Broca area activated.

It thus appears that the semantic and syntactic processes both activate a fronto-temporal network but the areas activated are different: in particular, the semantic processes seek the two hemispheres.

6.6 PRODUCTION OF ORAL LANGUAGE

The production of speech supposes articulatory motor processes, the programming of these motor processes, as well as processes relative to the rhythm of elocution.

The motor aspect of speech supposes coordinated movements of the bucco-phonatory sphere. Despite problems of speech observed in Broca's aphasia, Broca's area is not the region responsible for the execution of these articulatory movements: the motor areas (in the region in which the mouth and lips are represented) and premotor areas of the left hemisphere, including the supplementary motor area, the precentral gyrus and the insula in the most anterior part control this motor aspect of speech. The PET is in fact used to demonstrate that these regions are activated during the continuous recitation of figures or months of the year, while Broca's area is not activated during these tasks. On the other hand, Broca's area is activated when subjects are asked to think of words or to analyse phonemes (presented in visual or audial form) with or without production of speech.

In reality, it seems that Broca's area plays several roles. In the first place, with respect to speech, it is probably responsible for the programming of articulatory movements ensured by motor and premotor areas. It also seems responsible for the rhythm of elocution. Connected to the basal ganglia and the cerebellum, it also receives projections of numerous cortical sensory areas and sends projections towards the motor areas. These connections, this network, all together, probably explain its role in the rhythm of elocution.

More surprisingly, Broca's area could also play a role in syntax. In effect, although patients who have a lesion here have difficulties in verbal fluency, some of them, capable of speaking, display a discourse with deficient grammar characterized by an absence of verbs, pronouns, and conjunction and a phrase structure that is altogether deficient. In a correlative manner, these patients have difficulty in understanding certain phrases with difficult syntax, such as passive phrases in which the subject and the complement could be inversed (e.g., "the referee is pushed by the player"), even if their comprehension of simple phrases (unambiguous passive phrases such as "the ball is hit by the player" or active phrases such as "the player hits the ball") is not altered. In their joint work, Posner and Raichle (1994) reported a PET study showing that Broca's area is activated when the subject must generate a verb associated semantically with the word that is presented to him (e.g., the verb "to eat" associated with the presentation of the word "apple"). Other authors such as Damasio and Damasio (1992) also situate in Broca's area the centre of mediation of verbs. Finally, Broca's area seems implicated in the production—but also, perhaps, the comprehension— of phrase structure. It could be a site of syntactic assembly. Nevertheless, it should be emphasized that this role of Broca's area in the syntactic assembly is not unanimously agreed on by authors, some of them interpreting rather the activation of Broca's area in the grammatical processes as reflecting its implication in the phonological loop of working memory.

6.7 LATERALIZATION OF LANGUAGE

Since the discovery of the localization of Broca's and Wernicke's areas in the left hemisphere, it is conventional to consider that the areas responsible for treatment of oral language are located in the left hemisphere. Generally, the anatomical studies, whether they result from post mortem analysis or aMRI data, confirm that the regions implicated in language in the left hemisphere are sparsely or not present in the right hemisphere. In this connection, Broca's and Wernicke's areas have been cited already with notably the temporal planum, located on the surface of the temporal lobe but embedded in the Sylvian fissure, constituting the principal region of Wernicke's area. According to Geschwind and Levitsky (1968), the temporal planum is more developed in the left in 65% of subjects, while it is developed in the right in only 10% of subjects. These authors have also found that the difference could range in certain subjects up to a temporal planum five times as developed in the left than in the right. These variations of development of the temporal planum give rise to questions about the inter-individual differences in the matter of cerebral treatment of language and to a return to the role of the right hemisphere in language treatment.

6.7.1 The Role of the Right Hemisphere

In the first place, the right hemisphere intervenes in the perception of sensory inputs by which we understand language. Some authors advance even the idea that, with respect to the oral language, it is responsible for coding of vowels while the left hemisphere codes consonants. It also plays a role in access to vocabulary. Generally, the right hemisphere ensures the treatment of what can be called "indirect" language in which what is said (or written) must be understood differently (in the "second degree") as is the case with irony or metaphor. Thus, it has been possible to observe people with damage on the right brain who become incapable of interpreting such a language. We must also cite, among the functions of the right hemisphere, the treatment of prosody, the importance of which in oral language is underlined. All this is consistent, though it goes beyond that, with the role already mentioned of the right hemisphere in semantic treatment.

6.7.2 Inter-individual Differences

Some authors have sought more specifically the inter-individual differences in the lateralization of language. For example, a PET study of Tzourio-Mazoyer et al. (2004) specifically addressed inter-individual differences in the hemispheric organization of language. The authors assigned eight right-handed subjects and 12 left-handed subjects to listen to stories and to generate verbs linked semantically to words delivered orally. The authors thus calculated an index of hemispheric asymmetry for each of the tasks while observing the difference between the activations of right hemisphere and those of the left hemisphere.

On average, the functional index of asymmetry predominates on the left in all the regions activated by the two tasks. During the generation of verbs, it is manifested in regions of the triangular opercle and of the opercle of the inferior frontal gyrus, which confirms the role of Broca's area in the mediation of verbs. While the subjects were hearing the stories, this index manifested itself in the middle and inferior temporal regions.

Nevertheless, six subjects, including five left-handed subjects, out of the 20 studied, displayed an atypical asymmetry. In particular, a left-handed subject presented a right hemispheric asymmetry in the two tasks and another left-handed subject presented a different asymmetry for the two tasks (left for generation of verbs, right for listening to stories). The authors then carried out complementary analyses to characterize the typical subjects and the atypical subjects.

They concluded that in the typical subjects, the beginning of any language task is marked by a reconfiguration of the cerebral activity manifesting itself by an overall over-activation of the left hemisphere and an overall de-activation of the right hemisphere, following which specific regions of the task are activated (at left). But this reconfiguration does not seem to exist in the atypical subjects. In these latter, there would be either a difference of hemispheric specialization (case of the left-hander whose cerebral activation is that of an "inverted right-hander" for the two types of tasks), or a difference in the implication of both hemispheres as a function of the task: left hemisphere for one, right hemisphere for the other.

In conclusion, one can say that, since the discoveries of Broca and Wernicke, the models of cerebral treatment of language are considerably enriched by the study of several patients and by brain imaging. However, the mysteries of this function specific to humans are still far from being elucidated and no doubt the alliance of models of psycholinguistics and cognitive neuroscience will allow us to develop further our knowledge of treatment of language.

7

Attention

We have all had the experience of talking with a friend during the course of a party. If we look at this more closely, it seems strange. In fact a virtual brouhaha surrounds us, we are assailed by a wave of multiple stimulations, notably auditory (multiple conversations, noises of tinkling glass, bursts of laughter, music, ...), so that it is ultimately astonishing that this conversation could be carried on, all said and done, quite normally. This phenomenon was studied for the first time in 1953 by Cherry and has since been called the "cocktail party effect". It is one of our essential capacities, that is, selective attention that allows us to block out sound stimulations that do not concern us. In the same party, if suddenly a group of persons who are talking a bit further away, to which we pay no attention, pronounce for example the name of a friend, we hear it and thus can move our attention to listen to that conversation. This is the proof that something to which we pay no attention nevertheless reaches our brain in some manner or another, we are capable of testing the information that reaches us and choosing to treat only one part and, moreover, we can shift our attention. Note that this pertains not only to information issuing from the environment. We can also appear to listen to our interlocutor while being attentive to another conversation or our own thoughts.

These situations suggest a filtering of messages that reach us with a rejection of those that do not interest us. Does this filtering operate at the beginning of the chain of treatment (before which perceptive treatments are not realized) or later? We will see in the rest of this chapter that the two types of filtering probably coexist.

7.1 CONCEPTS ASSOCIATED WITH THE CONCEPT OF ATTENTION

The first definition of attention formulated in 1890 by James referred to selection and maintenance of a piece of information or a thought in consciousness. For a long time, scientists reasoned only in terms of early selection of the pertinent information. Without going as far back as the primary observations of Helmholtz (1894), we can cite Broadbent (1958), who first attempted to explain the "cocktail party" effect by his theory of selective filtering. According to this theory, humans are endowed with a unique channel of treatment of information. The limited capacity of this channel of treatment renders necessary the selection of the input from the channel of sensory information, before they can congest it. This early selection of information thus does not require perceptive treatment or, even less so, encoding, semantic treatment, etc.

But precisely the fact that one can shift one's attention, as when one turns the conversation after having heard the name of a friend in the preceding example, shows that the filtering cannot always be operated before the sensory information has begun to be treated. Other models have thus been elaborated following the works of Broadbent. According to the theory of attenuation of Treisman (1960), if the filtering is early it does not function in an "all or nothing" mode. The non-pertinent information is only treated less profoundly than the pertinent information. Deutsch and Deutsch (1963) advanced the hypothesis of a late selection, at the input of short-term memory. Broadbent himself admitted later (1970) that the non-pertinent information could nevertheless be transmitted by the channel of treatment but in an attenuated form. Indeed, from the 1970s onwards, the concepts of attentional resources and allocation of these resources to ongoing tasks were substituted for that of a single channel of treatment.

Thus, attention could be selected, sustained, oriented, shared, exogenous or endogenous. The attentional processes could be automatic or voluntary, conscious or unconscious. In conclusion, the attentional processes are multiple and we will see that they are underpinned by extensive neuronal networks, implying numerous cerebral regions.

7.2   VISUO-SPATIAL ATTENTION

7.2.1   The Posner and Raichle Model

The model was proposed following the implementation of a protocol elaborated by the team of Posner (Posner and Raichle, 1994) and now commonly used. The subject focuses on a point at the centre of a screen (and must do so throughout the trial): visual targets (light circles) are presented on it at right or left from this focal point for a very short time (15 ms), to which the subject must respond by pushing a button (right button for the target at right, left button for the target at left) as quickly as possible (reaction time situation, RT). But before the appearance of a target, an "index" (an arrow directed towards the right or left) is presented to the subject, indicating the side of the screen at which the target has more chances of appearing (probability of 80%). There are thus "valid" assays in which the location of the target agrees with the index, non-valid assays in which the target is presented on the side opposite to the direction indicated by the index, as well as neutral assays (in this case the index was a bidirectional arrow not indicating any particular direction). The RTs observed were shorter in the "valid" condition than in the "neutral" condition, which in turn were shorter than the RTs observed in the "non-valid" condition. The index may thus represent a benefit or, on the contrary, a cost, depending on its validity. The subjects must constantly focus on the central point, there is no shifting of the glance and the effect observed on the RT thus translates into an acceleration of perceptive processes and, perhaps, of the decision on the response to be brought in. This acceleration of perceptive and decisional processes is interpreted as resulting from an unconscious shift in visual attention in the region of the space indicated by the index, to detect the target more rapidly. For Posner, this process flows from early and endogenous attentional processes (the subject directs his attention in a direction of space) and is translated into an accentuation of the internal representation of stimulus to the place expected, which accelerates his perception when it appears.

But the visuo-spatial attention can also be oriented in an exogenous manner and can give rise to a phenomenon called *return inhibition*. For example, if the subject is presented with a succession of visual targets in various places in the visual field, the RT proves shorter on a target presented at the same place as the preceding target, which indicates an automatic exogenous orientation of attention: the attention of the subject is "caught" by the target. But it is important to note that this effect is observed only if the two targets are presented after a very short lapse in time (between 50 and 250 ms). Beyond that, it is the inverse phenomenon that is observed: the RT on a target presented at the same place as the preceding target (in a delay greater than 250 ms) is higher than the RT on a target presented at any place. It is this phenomenon that is called return inhibition: when the delay between two targets is relatively long, the attention of the subject is no longer caught by the preceding target and the reorientation of his attention towards this region becomes difficult (it is inhibited). This phenomenon of inhibition can probably be explained in terms of the time necessary for the recapture of neuromediators liberated in the synaptic space: the neuronal networks influencing the networks of perception (and making thus synapses with their neurons) liberating their neuromediators at the synaptic level cannot be reactive before this recapture. Moreover, this phenomenon arises from a necessity. In effect, to the extent that our attention can be captured and oriented automatically by all sorts of stimuli, it is useful that this process be limited in time: in daily life, a prolonged maintenance of attention thus "caught" on stimuli that are eventually non-pertinent would prevent us from being attentive to other pertinent stimuli.

For Posner and Raichle (1994), the visuo-spatial attention flows thus from the coexistence of two types of process: an exogenous process activated automatically by the index and an endogenous process put into play when the subject voluntarily carries his attention to one or another region of space. Their model of attention postulates the existence of a series of mental operations as follows: a primary stage of attentional alert corresponding to "capture" of attention by the index (automatic process), a stage of interruption of attention, the localization of the target, the disengagement of attention of the spatial region indicated by the index, the "movement" towards the placement of the target and the engagement of attention (controlled process) on this target, accompanied by a return inhibition of attention on the region indicated by the index.

Data from neuropsychology and functional brain imaging confirm this model of automatic and voluntary attentional processes.

7.2.2 Contribution of Neuropsychology: Semi-negligence

Semi-negligence, a syndrome in which the patient ignores objects, persons, and the half of their body located in the same general hemifield, is a problem that numerous studies have shown to arise from attentional processes rather than from perceptive or motor processes. Semi-negligent patients are carriers of a lesion, generally on the right (their semi-negligence concerns the left hemifield), including the inferior parietal region and the temporo-parietal region, Posner and Raichle (1994) described the case of a patient (an artist) injured in the right parietal cortex following a cerebral vascular accident (CVA). The self-portraits drawn by this artist in the first weeks following the CVA showed negligence of the entire left part of his face.[1] The numerous studies dedicated to semi-negligence reveal that the performances of these patients at various tasks to which one can subject them differ according to the extent of the lesion, the type of response, and other factors. These differences have been interpreted by the authors in various terms: problems of automatic orientation of attention, difficulty in disengaging their attention on the ipsilateral side to engage it towards the contro-lateral side, bias of exogenous attention in favour of the ipsilateral side without equivalent bias with respect to the endogenous attention (for review see Sieroff, 2004).

7.2.3 The Contribution of PET and fMRI

Brain imaging has made it possible to clarify to some extent, even to reconcile, these various interpretations. In a PET study, Corbetta et al. (1993) studied the cerebral activations generated by endogenous attention and exogenous attention. The authors thus showed an increase of activity in the superior portion of the parietal lobe and of the frontal lobe. More precisely, the increase in activity at the superior parietal lobe was produced during changes in orientation of attention, whether changes of endogenous origin, i.e., voluntary, or exogenous origin, automatic. The authors observed that when the attention was shifted towards the left, the activity at the superior parietal lobe increased, but, very interestingly, they observed that when the attention was shifted towards the right, the increase in cerebral activity involved the left superior parietal lobe and the right superior parietal lobe (see Fig. 7.1).

The authors deduced from this that the superior parietal lobe, more particularly that of the right hemisphere, plays the principal role in the spatial orientation of attention, a result confirmed subsequently by various authors.

In an fMRI study, Corbetta et al. (2000) refined the implication of various regions of the right parietal lobe: the intra-parietal groove for the spatial orientation of attention, and the temporo-parietal junction for the detection of the target, particularly when this persists in a region of space different from that on which attention was directed. These data explain why

---

[1] The progress of this patient revealed through his self-portraits showed gradual recovery post-CVA, his drawings becoming more complete over the next few months until he drew a complete self-portrait (including the left part of his face) at nine months after the CVA.

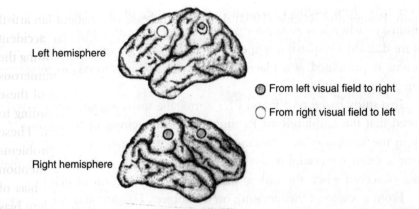

Left hemisphere

◉ From left visual field to right

○ From right visual field to left

Right hemisphere

Fig. 7.1 Cerebral activations during changes in orientation of attention (Corbetta et al., 1993). The shifting of attention from the right towards the left activates the superior parietal lobe of the right hemisphere. The shifting of attention from the left to the right activates the superior parietal lobe of both hemispheres.

patients who have lesions at the temporo-parietal junction show difficulties in disengaging their attention from one point to direct it towards another (Friedrich et al. 1998) and why a lesion on the right takes a greater toll than one on the left (Perry and Zecky, 2000).

7.3 SELECTIVE ATTENTION: VISUAL/AUDITORY

7.3.1 Modifications in Sensory Inputs

Hillyard was the first to discover the existence of evoked potential marking the beginning of attentional processes (Hilyard et al., 1973). In a task of dichotic listing in which different sounds are sent, each into one ear, and in which the instructions to the subject are to pay attention to the sound reaching one of the two ears, the authors showed the existence of an early negative wave, lasting around 100 ms after the stimulus (N1 wave), the amplitude of which is greater for the stimuli to which the subject pays attention than for the others. This effect is called the "N1 effect". This wave is an exogenous wave, the sensory origin of which is deduced from its latency, short and highly reproducible. Subsequently, other studies made it possible to establish that this wave was generated at the level of the auditory cortex. A positive wave of the same type (P1 wave) persisting in lateral occipital regions is observed during the presentation of visual stimuli. The P1 wave is also modulated by attention. Although it is not modulated when attention is given to the colour, spatial frequency or orientation of visual stimulus, or when it is given to a precise object presented in a visual scene, it is modulated by spatial attention: the P1 wave is greater when the visual stimulus is presented at a place to which the subject directs his attention (Mangun et al., 1993).

In a study based on EP and PET simultaneously, Mangun et al. (1997) showed that the amplitude of P1 and that of the activity of fusiform gyrus vary in the same way as a function of the attention given to visual stimuli during a relatively complex task (pairing of symbols), a phenomenon that is not observed when the task is much simpler (detection of light).

From a review of the literature on the subject, Hillyard and Anllo-Vento (1998) showed that the influence of visual attention intervened on EP from 75 ms post-stimulus onward, while going beyond this interval. They thus suggested a primary effect linked to spatial attention and a second effect linked to selective attention on certain properties of the visual object selected in the preceding step. There would thus be an advantage, expressed in a gain in time, of visual attention to the region of interest because the object expected will stimulate the system of visual treatment before the others. This temporal advantage could increase to the extent that the visual information progresses in the cerebral structures that treat it. This would have the consequence that, for some time, only the visual information of the object selected by the attention would be treated by the neuronal chain and this, from the striate cortex to the extra-striate cortex up to the infero-temporal cortex.

The question of the similarity of processes in the visual modality and in the auditory modality (or in other sensory modalities) may not be entirely resolved, but the authors presently lean towards a similarity of intervention of selective attention: this modifies the sensory information to their "input" in the striate cortex.

The question that arises is the following: What cerebral structures act thus on the striate cortex so early in the chain of perceptive treatment?

Experiments carried out on animals (with microelectrodes implanted in various cerebral structures) have made it possible to draw solid hypotheses that have been confirmed in humans by studies in brain imaging. A complex cerebral network seems thus implicated in selective attention.

This network could comprise the following (Corbetta et al., 1990; Heinze et al., 1994; Aleln et al., 1997; Pugh et al., 1996):

—the prefrontal cortex

—the parietal lobe, mostly its inferior part, and

—the anterior portion of the cingular gyrus, the pulvinar of the thalamus and the cerebellum.

These various structures likely play different roles ranging from the activation of the striate cortex to the maintenance in working memory of information to which attention is given and the inhibition of information that is not given attention. In Chapter 4, the pulvinar has been mentioned as not being part of the pathways from the retina to the striate cortex. But it maintains reciprocal relationships with the frontal cortex and the parietal cortex, with the sensory extra-striate cortex and with the subcortical structures. It could thus constitute a relay allowing the frontal cortex and the parietal cortex to influence the treatments realized within the extra-striate cortex.

7.3.2 Chronometry of Attentional Processes: Support of EP

The low temporal precision of PET and, to a lesser extent, of fMRI does not allow fine measurement of the temporal course of the intervention of these various structures. In particular, it does not allow us to distinguish between what flows from automatic processes and what flows from voluntary processes, in that these processes succeed each other very rapidly, or even occur in parallel. For that, only EP is available.

(a) *Preparation*

Among the series of waves marking the progression of attentional processes, we can cite, in the first place, the negative contingent variation (NCV) that persists in the frontal or fronto-central region and is present only when the subject waits for a stimulus to which it must bring a motor response. The NCV thus marks preparatory attentional processes linked to the time that passes and that stops from the time the stimulus calling for a response has been delivered. The NCV does not develop if the subject cannot estimate the moment at which the stimulus will be delivered or if the stimulus he is waiting for requires no treatment or particular motor response on his part. The NCV seems generated by the frontal regions.

(b) *Automatic detection of change*

Beyond the NCV and preparatory processes to the action it marks, other waves more specifically mark automatic attentional processes. Previously, the concepts of automatic and controlled attentional processes were mentioned with the works of Posner and Raichle (1994) relative to visuo-spatial attention. The automatic processes have also been addressed with the N1 effect. The protocol of dichotic listening was thus applied in numerous studies. In particular, it was coupled with the oddball paradigm intercalating rare stimuli (targets) among a succession of frequent stimuli in numerous studies carried out by Naatanen (for review, see Naatanen, 1992). In such a situation, N100 is followed, between 100 and 200 ms post-stimulus, by a more ample negativity for rare stimuli, denominated N2a or mismatch negativity (MMN). The MMN is sensitive to differences between the two stimuli that pertain to the frequency (pitch of sound), intensity, duration, and spatial localization of two stimuli, even if the difference is not perceptible consciously. It culminates in the fronto-central region and is more ample on the right hemisphere than on the left hemisphere no matter what side (ear) is stimulated. Studies designed to reconstitute the cerebral sources of this wave have shown that it was generated by the auditory temporal cortex (bilateral) and by the right frontal (or prefrontal) cortex (Girard et al., 1990). The temporal regions will detect the target-stimulus different from the preceding ones, by the analysis of its physical characteristics, and it is the right prefrontal cortex that automatically will trigger the processes of detection of change.

(c) *Automatic orientation of attention*
The MMN is generally followed by a positive wave (P3a) in the fronto-central region (250-350 ms post-stimulus) that has been the subject of a large number of studies. Donchin (1981) described it as a wave marking the surprise engendered by a stimulus that is new, rare, incongruous and in any case unexpected in the context of preceding stimuli. It is present, in the same region, as much in its auditory modality as in its visual modality and its amplitude is large to the extent that the stimulus is rare. Thus, the treatment of this rare stimulus demands an allocation of attentional resources that is greater than the treatment of an expected stimulus and it is this that is manifested in the increase of amplitude of the P3a (Johnson, 1988). The P3a appears thus like a wave marking the automatic (involuntary) change of orientation of attention to the new and unexpected stimulus.

Finally, the automatic attentional processes are object of a series of waves that succeed in time and mark their progress: automatic detection of changes, based on the analysis of physical characteristics of the stimulus (N1 or P1, then MMN) in the temporal region (for auditory stimuli, occipital for visual stimuli) and the right frontal region, and then the automatic orientation of attention towards this stimulus (P3a) in the frontal and parietal regions.

(d) *Controlled orientation of attention*
After the waves marking the automatic attentional processes, the N2b persists when the subject has received an explicit instruction of attention, either directly or indirectly in the form of specific responses to be given on the

stimulus or stimuli (Naatanen and Gaillard, 1983). It develops, 200 to 250 ms post-stimulus, in the central region, a topography not sensitive to the sensory modality through which the stimuli are conveyed. It is generally followed by a positive wave that develops 350 to 600 ms post-stimulus in the parietal region (P3b). The appearance of these waves is linked to the voluntary attentional engagement of the subject necessitated by the task (explicit instruction for attention to a stimulus, discrimination between several stimuli with associated responses different for each of these stimuli). The very rich literature on these two waves and their variations as to amplitude and latency, as a function of characteristics of the task, is based on various interpretations as to processes marked by these waves. One can cite notably processes of evaluation and categorization of stimulus for the N2b, selection and choice of response, or updating of working memory for the P3b. In any case, it seems clear that these two waves are linked to the attention oriented and controlled toward the stimulus being treated. As in the case of other waves, there is no consensus on the cerebral regions generating these two waves. The anterior cingular gyrus seems nevertheless implicated in both cases.

7.4 THE CEREBRAL MODELS OF ATTENTION

Several models have been advanced to take into account attentional processes, but here we cite only some that have served to refine the supposed role of various cerebral structures.

The Posner model, elaborated within the context of Posner's works on visuo-spatial attention and taken up again in his work co-authored with Raichle (1994), postulated the existence of three attentional networks: a posterior network, an anterior network and a vigilance network. The posterior network ensures spatial orientation of attention and will comprise the posterior parietal cortex, the pulvinar, and the superior colliculus. The parietal cortex will be implicated in the disengagement of attention oriented on a region of space, the superior colliculus will allow the displacement of attention towards a new spatial region, and the pulvinar will ensure the engagement of attention on this new region. The anterior network will comprise the cingular cortex controlling the detection of the visual object and the supplementary motor area for its role in the programming of the adequate motor response. Finally, the vigilance network will comprise the coeruleus locus of the cerebral trunk and the connections of this structure, notably with the right frontal cortex. Taking into account the neuromediator characteristic of these connections, this network of vigilance is called the *noradrenergetic system* of the coeruleus locus. Selective attention, piloted by the posterior network, will thus be distinct from the attentional command piloted by the anterior network. Thus, these three networks will be entirely individualized and will control clearly distinct attentional processes. They will nevertheless be interconnected.

The Mesulam (1990) model includes the same cerebral structures as that of Posner, but proposes a different organization of their relationships and processes that they control. This model distinguishes three large regions: the superior parietal cortex, the cingular cortex and the frontal oculomotor field, a region of the prefrontal cortex corresponding to the Brodmann area 8, also called "frontal eye field" (FEF). These three regions are controlled upstream by the reticulated formation of the cerebral trunk implicated in the level of arousal. This model postulates the existence of an internal representation of the exterior world in the form of a perceptive chart localized in the parietal region. The cingular gyrus distributes the spatial attention, while the frontal oculomotor field takes charge of the programming of movements of exploration, pursuit, and visual fixation. The attention itself implicates the frontal cortical, cingular and parietal regions, but these regions are themselves connected with other cortical structures (infero-temporal cortex, orbito-frontal cortex) and subcortical structures (striatum, pulvinar).

We can also cite the model of LaBerge et al. (2000) in which attentional control arises from the prefrontal regions and attentional filtering is ensured by the pulvinar of the thalamus, while the expression of attention arises from the posterior cortical regions: the parietal cortex for tasks involving location of a target, and the infero-temporal cortex for tasks of identification of objects.

Finally, the model of Corbetta and Shulman (2002) postulates the existence of two fronto-parietal networks (see Fig. 7.2): the superior network

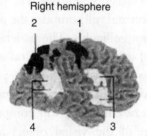

Right hemisphere

1 + 2: Dorsal fronto-parietal network

3 + 4: Ventral fronto-parietal network

Fig. 7.2 The attentional model of Corbetta et al. (2002). It includes the dorsal fronto-parietal network (1 + 2) and the ventral fronto-parietal network (3 + 4). 1, frontal eye field (FEF); 2, superior parietal lobule and intraparietal sulcus; 3, ventral frontal cortex (inferior frontal gyrus and middle frontal gyrus); 4, temporo-parietal junction (inferior parietal lobule and superior temporal gyrus).

and the inferior network. The superior fronto-parietal (or dorsal fronto-parietal) network is bilateral and controls the endogenous attentional processes. The inferior fronto-parietal network concerns only the right hemisphere and includes the temporo-parietal junction and the ventral frontal cortex: it controls the exogenous attentional processes.

Beyond this diversity in the attentional models, these models agree nevertheless in the implication of a certain number of cerebral structures in attentional processes: the prefrontal cortex (the right especially), the parietal cortex, the cingular gyrus, the pulvinar, as well as the activator structures of the cerebral trunk.

Hemispheric Specialization and Differences between Male Brain and Female Brain

Broca's area—more generally the cerebral treatment of language—is undoubtedly the most frequent example cited to illustrate the fact that the right brain and the left brain are not organized identically and that there is a functional asymmetry between the two hemispheres. Yet, the differences go well beyond areas of language. Part of what we discuss here takes up again certain data mentioned in the preceding chapters. In this chapter we add other data. We also mention neurobiological data most often advanced to explain this hemispheric asymmetry. Finally, we address the differences linked to gender in this hemispheric asymmetry.

8.1 HEMISPHERIC ASYMMETRY

8.1.1 The Left Hemisphere and the Notion of Dominant Hemisphere

Following the discovery of the lateralization of language to the left in the 19th century, for a long time the left hemisphere was thought to be the "dominant" hemisphere. Without taking up here all the data discussed in Chapter 6, let us recall simply the fact that Broca's area does not exist in the right hemisphere (for the immense majority of the population) and that anatomists have largely proved asymmetry, in favour of the left hemisphere, of the temporal planum of Wernicke's area. Let us not forget, however, that several studies including that of Tzourio-Mazoyer et al. (2004) have shown inter-individual differences to which we will return, notably when we treat differences between the male brain and the female brain.

In any case, at the time of Broca and Wernicke and up to a relatively recent period, the prevailing ideas were that (1) language is a specific function of humans and human thought, (2) hemispheric specialization is peculiar to humans (we will see that this is not entirely so), and (3) since the left hemisphere is that of language and since language is peculiar to humans, it is thus "dominant". The fact that the manual preference of the majority of the population is expressed on the right side—which is controlled by the left hemisphere—only supported this conception. One cannot refrain from mentioning the prejudices that this notion of "dominance" has led to, since it has largely contributed to the idea of left-handedness as an "abnormality".

Regarding manual preference, on the whole, in light of studies carried out on large samples, it seems that right-handers represent around 90% of the population, no matter what their socio-cultural origin. The fact that this proportion is of the same order in all cultures is significant: it means that the type of writing—from left to right, right to left, or up to down—is not responsible for this manual preference. But manual preference still does not signify complete laterality. In fact, if one takes into account all the activities of modern life, it seems that the percentage of "pure" right-handers drops to 70%. Questionnaires such as the Edinburgh Handedness Inventory allow us to assess the actual laterality of an individual. In fact, one may be a right-hander for writing but not for dealing cards or be a right-hander for the hand but have a left eye as the director eye or even start climbing stairs with the left foot. For example, between the pure left-handers (around 10% of the population) and the pure right-handers, we find persons who are more or less right-handers or more or less left-handers, in a proportion of 20% of the population. That being so, the socio-cultural impact is undeniable since the percentage of "pure" left-handers tends to increase with the change in attitude with respect to left-handedness: it is higher today in young people (nearly 15%) than in older people (around 6%).

The connection between manual preference and lateralization of language is easily observed in patients who, following a cerebral vascular accident affecting the left hemisphere, become simultaneously aphasic and hemiplegic (more or less significant paralysis of the right side).

8.1.2 Methods of Highlighting Hemispheric Differences in Humans

At present, the preferred methods for highlighting differences that are anatomical as well as functional between the two hemispheres are obviously neuropsychological case studies and methods of anatomical and functional brain imaging. Let us emphasize, however, that these two types of methods do not pertain to all responses. Researchers are in fact faced with numerous questions. For example, when bilateral activations are observed that are, however, more significant on one side, the following questions must be asked: is the function or the process studied taken in charge by the hemisphere in which the activation is greater (the less important activation on the other hemisphere will result from a simple transfer of inter-hemispheric information, or even of a simple artefact linked to the method) or does each of the two hemispheres play a specific role even if one of them plays a more important role? Moreover, the same principle of reconstruction of images from signals emitted does not allow us to know precisely whether the cerebral activations highlighted are related to the white matter or grey matter, particularly for PET and EP but also, to a certain extent, for fMRI. The question is particularly important when we seek to determine what flows from the cerebral activity of one hemisphere and what flows from the transmission of signals from one hemisphere to another.

Other methods have been used—and in some cases still are. These pertain to strictly anatomical studies of post mortem autopsies. Moreover, in the past (in the 1930s), some neurosurgeons, such as the team of Penfield, used a method of electro-stimulation of various cerebral regions. The operation—which still necessitated the opening of the cranial box and meninges!—was achieved under local anaesthesia so well that the patient could describe what he saw and heard during each stimulation. This highly invasive method was of course abandoned for obvious ethical reasons but it allowed a great deal of progress in the field of brain mapping. Subsequently, in the 1960s, functional brain organization was largely studied by means of the "split-brain" model (described in Chapter 6) and the Wada test.

The Wada test was developed by Wada and Rasmussen (1960). It involved a method of temporary anaesthesia of one side of the brain by injection of an anaesthetic with brief action in a carotid artery. The temporary anaesthesia of the hemisphere produced the same effects as those of a brain lesion of one hemisphere, but for a short time. The researchers could thus observe the deficiencies consecutive to this anaesthesia. In achieving the reverse operation (anaesthesia of the other hemisphere), conclusions could be drawn as to the respective roles of each of the hemispheres in the function studied. A problem remains, nevertheless, as to the role of cooperation between hemispheres.

8.1.3 Hemispheric Specialization: Review of the Respective Roles of the Two Hemispheres

Contrary to what we may believe, humans are not the only ones to display a manual preference and, thus, a hemispheric "dominance". It is presently known that animals such as the ape as well as the cat preferentially use one paw rather than the other to catch prey. Nevertheless, contrary to what has been observed in humans, we find the same proportion of animals using preferentially the left paw or the right paw. Moreover, it is not even certain that this preference is identical for all the tasks the animal performs. Besides, in some apes that display a primitive form of "language" in the form of vocal "codes", it seems that this function is controlled by the left hemisphere. Again, song birds (those that are capable of learning different songs of simple innate vocalizations, seem also to show a lateralization—to the left— of structures controlling this song. It is to be noted that, among song birds, only males have this capacity to learn and it is only among them that one observes the important development of cerebral structures implicated in this learning. In conclusion, even though these results are fragmentary, they tend to show that hemispheric specialization is not strictly limited to humans.

In the preceding chapters, the respective roles of the two hemispheres are discussed in terms of various developments. We therefore offer here only a highly synthetic summary of the "specialities" of each hemisphere.

Concerning the sensory and motor aspects, we know that, overall, the left half of the body corresponds to the right hemisphere and vice versa. For example, visual information from the left visual field is transported to the right primary visual cortex, while visual information from the right visual field is transported to the left primary visual cortex. Similarly, the movement of limbs of the right side are controlled by the left motor cortex and vice versa.

But it is probably at the level of associative areas that the distinction between the two hemispheres operates. And it is also at this level that the linkage between the two hemispheres comes into full play. This is ensured by bundles of fibres, of which the callous body is the most important

(200 million fibres). Indeed, the correspondence, very strong for associative areas, is less so for sensory or motor primary areas.

Although the left hemisphere is associated with language and manual preference, as we have already seen, recall nevertheless that the right hemisphere participates in certain treatments of language such as those linked to semantics or prosody.

Concerning the right hemisphere, its essential functions listed to date concern visuo-spatial tasks, particularly those that require mental rotation, recognition of familiar faces (probably linked with its perceptive-mnesic function), and emotions. This does not mean that the left hemisphere does not play a role in these functions but just that the right hemisphere probably plays the principal role.

8.2 DIFFERENCES BETWEEN MEN AND WOMEN

8.2.1 Do Men and Women have Different Cognitive Capacities?

In a popular work, A. and B. Pease (1999) suggested in an eye-catching title that men never listen and women cannot read road maps. They drew up a catalogue of activities in which men succeed while women fail, and vice versa. Although we all know people corresponding perfectly to their caricatures, we can also cite cases corresponding to the inverse caricature. And most of all, we know a multitude of men and women who fall between the two extremes. Indeed, the analysis of the literature reveals that the situation is much more nuanced than what these two authors lead us to believe.

It is the verbal and visuo-spatial capacities that have been the subject of the largest number of studies on the cognitive differences between men and women. Doreen Kimura (2001) was one of the authors who have worked most extensively on these differences. Yet, the study of the literature, including her own works, often reveals only minimal differences on certain highly targeted proofs, involving, moreover, only some individuals.

It is common to affirm a superiority of women in the verbal domain. This ultimately seems to concern only some tasks such as enunciating the maximum number of words beginning with the same letter, rapidly articulating complex words, discriminating the sounds of vowels and consonants, and finding words in long-term memory. Women are also perform better in tasks of pairing items or association of ideas but there is no clear difference between men and women on tests of comprehension or verbal reasoning. Still, we must specify that the superiority of women in verbal tasks is observed only in some women (two out of three or three out of four, generally).

Inversely, it is generally considered that men perform better than women in visuo-spatial tasks that require precision of direction (e.g., shooting arrows or intercepting a projectile) and that require a mental rotation and/ or a three-dimensional vision of an object represented in a plan (two-dimensional space). In fact, the meta-analyses of Linn and Peterson (1985) and of Voyer et al. (1995) have shown that it is really only in mental rotation that men are better than women; even this is not true in all proofs of mental rotation and mostly, for each proof, we find around one woman out of four who surpasses the men.

These global differences between men and women in verbal and visuo-spatial domains can be summarized by the observation of Dabbs et al. (1998) according to which, to indicate a direction, men are more "abstract" than women: they use terms of Euclidean geometry, cardinal points, distances; women use concrete landmarks, they use notions of right and left, and so on. In sum, according to the data of Dabbs et al. (1998), men voluntarily draw a plan while women use words to describe the route to be taken. Nevertheless, such a summary is also slightly caricaturistic, since, in the different sub-tasks of language or visuo-spatial ability, the two sexes alternately argue over superiority and since the effects of groups—when they exist—are not found in all individuals.

Some differences have also been observed in the domain of facial recognition and decoding of emotional expressions. Here also, many inconsistencies are observed between the studies, which could be due to the weakness of samples on which they are based as much as to the heterogeneity of individual behaviour. It will be recalled (Chapter 4) that facial recognition is one of the non-verbal capacities that could be specific to the right hemisphere. Prosopagnosy is evidenced consequent to a lesion of the right hemisphere, and studies based on the tachistoscopic presentation of faces in the right or left hemifield show that faces presented in the left visual hemifield are treated more rapidly than faces presented in the right hemifield. But certain authors have observed this only in some men. Moreover, the superiority of the right hemisphere for facial treatment is seen only when the face is treated holistically, the left hemisphere prevailing when the treatment of the face is done analytically (Parkin and Williamson, 1987). Generally, overall, differences are not observed in performance between men and women in facial recognition. On the other hand, differences could exist in the domain of recognition of facial expressions. Women seem to have an advantage over men in decoding emotional expressions (Rosenthal et al., 1979; Hall, 1984), but this difference concerns mostly feminine faces, since they are more expressive than masculine faces (Wagner et al., 1993). Moreover, all emotions do not give rise to the same differences. In fact, according to Wagner et al. (1993), men recognize better than women the expression of anger expressed by a male face, but there is no difference between men and women in recognizing this expression of anger on a feminine face or in recognizing a positive expression (joy). For other negative expressions (disgust, fear, sorrow), it is on the contrary women who have greater sensitivity, whether the face is that of a man or a woman. It is seen here also that no clear-cut difference appears between men and women.

Some authors (Geary, 1998) have attempted to explain the differences between men and women in anthropo-phylogenetic terms: the distant past of men charged with hunting (wild animals) and constrained for this purpose to locate something in space (forest, jungle), the need for them to decode the expression of anger in other men in relation with the need to "defend their territory"; on the contrary, the development of language capacities in women living in groups of women, and of their capacities to decode non-verbal signals (emotions) in relation to their maternal role in having to understand the internal state and needs of their children. No matter how seductive this interpretation, it remains a hypothesis.

In conclusion, we can say that the differences observed in various domains (language, visuo-spatial, faces, emotional expressions) probably arise more from strategies of use of cognitive capacities than from the capacities themselves. This is not without consequence for the cerebral organization that could differ between men and women but could also be identical, the difference lying rather in the cerebral functioning—and not in the anatomy—or more precisely on the promptings of various cerebral structures, and more particularly the two cerebral hemispheres, which could differ according to the strategies of treatment, variable from one individual to another and more particularly between men and women. A result that is based on this functional hypothesis concerns the effects of levels of steroid hormones on performance. Several studies have supported the idea that the performances of women varies during the menstrual cycle. It has been shown that their verbal performance is greatest when their level of estradiol is high (just before ovulation), while their spatial ability is minimal during this period and maximal during menstruation (Kimura, 2001). In rats, studies on spatial orientation in a maze have given the same type of results. Moreover, it has also been shown in humans that seasonal and daily variations of the testosterone level (higher in autumn than in spring, higher in the morning than in the evening) seem also associated with variations of performance on spatial tests. An improvement has even been shown in working memory in older males by means of a complementary input of testosterone, without reaching an equivalent result in women by an input of estrogen (Janowsky et al., 2000). Such relationships between levels of circulating steroid hormones and performances help to boost the hypothesis of a different functioning of men and women rather than that of different aptitudes linked to cerebral anatomical differences that are well established.

8.2.2   What are the Differences between the Male and Female Brain?

Some differences linked to gender exist in relation to sexual behaviour. They will not be addressed here since we mention only differences linked to cognitive functions. Nevertheless, we must mention the influence of steroid hormones on the development of the nervous system, for the foetus as well as during the course of development, including daily or rather periodic variations in their levels. Some experiments carried out on animals (rats, song birds) and based on hormonal manipulations have made it possible to support this hypothesis of hormonal influence on the development of the brain. However, overall, there is no equivalent data in humans. Testosterone—to which both sexes are exposed over the course of intra-uterine development—slows the development of certain parts of the left hemisphere during foetal life. The regions corresponding to the right hemisphere develop so much faster that one talks of earlier maturation of the right hemisphere. This phenomenon could be accentuated in some individuals, which thus favours an inversion of laterality. The fact that male foetuses are more exposed to testosterone could thus explain that the frequency of left-handers is higher in men than in women (around two-thirds of left-handers are men). Some have profited from this to advance various hypotheses of particular competences (e.g., mathematics) in left-handers (males, obviously) to the "dominant" right hemisphere: none of these has to date been demonstrated. If testosterone appears implicated in the dimorphism of the two hemispheres, estradiol influences the density of dendritic spines. The phenomenon has been shown for neurons of the hippocampus in the rat but the underlying mechanisms are still poorly understood: estradiol could reduce the production of GABA (inhibitory neurotransmitter) by the inhibitor neurons and thus reduce the presynaptic inhibition; this favours the activity of hippocampic pyramidal cells and the development of their dendritic spines. For the present, it is not known whether this phenomenon applies equally to other regions of the brain or whether it also pertains to humans. Besides, it seems that steroid hormones interact with the genetic factors so that the cellular receptors of "male" neurons (carriers of a pair of chromosomes

XY) and "female" neurons (carriers of a pair of chromosomes XX) do not impregnate different hormones in the same way.

(a) *The volume of the brain*

One incontestable difference between men and women concerns the cerebral volume (slightly higher by just under 10% in men). The essence of this difference is undoubtedly attributable to differences in size of individuals. We must strongly emphasize here that no serious study has ever allowed the correlation of cerebral volume to cognitive performance or more generally to intelligence. The ratio is significant: in the 19th century, some anatomists (including Broca) concluded the superiority of white men over black men or that of men over women on the basis of differences of cerebral volume and we know that such a belief was the basis of racist theories.

Since the advent of methods of brain imaging, some studies have all the same sought to know what the significance is of difference in brain volume—apart from that relating to the size of individuals. Their results are entirely contradictory. Some authors find intra-cranial space smaller in women, others find more white matter in men, still others find more grey matter in women. For Nopoulos et al. (2000) the quantities of white matter and grey matter are overall the same in men and in women but the latter have more grey matter in the right parietal lobe, which the authors attribute to the effects of steroid hormones during the course of development. Gur et al. (1999) posited that in men—and not in women—there is more grey matter in the left hemisphere than in the right. It is seen that there are various and inconsistent data available that reflect the limits of methods of measuring the various constituents of the brain and more particularly methods of counting neurons, despite the emergence of magnetic resonance. Interestingly, Gur et al. (1999) attempted to relate the possible differences of grey matter and white matter in terms of treatment (grey matter) and transmission (white matter) of information useful for the accomplishment of cognitive tasks, whether within one hemisphere or from one hemisphere to another.

(b) *Asymmetries between and within hemispheres*

The regions that have been particularly studied above all pertain to language, about which behavioural studies suggest certain differences between men and women: first the temporal cortex—in particular the Sylvian fissure and the temporal planum—and Broca's area but also the callous body for its function of communication between the two hemispheres.

Starting from the observation that women seem less struck with aphasia following a left lesion, Kimura (2001) analysed in detail the case of 32 patients and 49 patients with such a lesion. She demonstrated that the probability of suffering aphasia was greater after the left anterior frontal regions were affected in women and left posterior frontal regions were affected in men. She concluded from this that the areas of language located in the left frontal region (Broca's area) were more anterior in women than in men, which, taking into account the architecture of a network of blood irrigation in the brain, exposes them less to cerebral vascular accidents in the region of Broca's area. That suggests differences between men and women at the level of volumes of anterior brain and posterior brain, the position of Broca's area, and the Sylvian fissure. The data in the literature are not entirely in agreement on this question. There is, for example, a study (Haratsy et al., 1997) based on post mortem autopsies carried out on 10 men and 11 women that shows effectively a greater volume of Broca's area, temporal planum and left superior temporal gyrus (Wernicke's area) in women. There is also a magnetic resonance study (Steinmetz et al., 1995) showing that the volume of the anterior brain is greater in women. On the other hand, with respect to the Sylvian fissure, Foundas et al. (1999) in a study also based on magnetic resonance found it more posterior in the left hemisphere (that of Broca's area), but in men as well as in women. This does not rule out, nevertheless, that it might be more posterior in women as suggested by other authors.

With respect to Wernicke's area, if the left inferior parietal lobule is more voluminous at left than at right, this asymmetry will be less marked in women (Frederikse et al., 1999). An interesting study relates the volume of the temporal planum and that of the callous body. This involved a series of post mortem autopsies (Aboitiz et al. 1992) realized on 20 men and 20 women, all right-handed, which led to a negative correlation between the size of the temporal planum and that of the middle part of the callous body: according to these authors, language could, in some individuals, depend on both hemispheres but in this case, the left temporal planum is less extended and the inter-hemispheric communication is greater.

Indeed, several studies report a larger callous body in women. Having analysed in detail, by means of magnetic resonance, the different parts of the callous bodies on a large number of subjects (122 young adults), Allen et al. (1991) concluded that it is the posterior part of the callous body (the splenium) that is larger in women. Note that a result of the same type was found in the rat (Kim et al. 1996), with a higher density of axons in the female at the splenium. Another bundle of fibres linking the two hemispheres— the anterior commissure—seems also larger in women (Allen and Gorski, 1991). These data on the callous bodies and the anterior commissure thus suggest a difference between men and women in the cooperation between the two hemispheres with a lateralization less marked in women.

Several series of results from brain imaging and EEG confirm this hypothesis. For example, the team of Corsi-Cabrera (Corsi-Cabrera et al., 1989, 1997) studied the EEG emitted in the band of alpha frequency (8–12 Hz) and thus showed a greater similarity of EEG on the two hemispheres in women than in men. They also showed that, within the right hemisphere, the EEG activities recorded at the temporal level and at the frontal level were more strongly correlated in men than in women. For these authors, it is the larger hemispheric specialization (manifesting itself here at right by the correlation of EEG at the temporal and frontal level) that explains the larger visuo-spatial ability of men. Through a PET study, Azzari et al. (1995) also concluded greater interhemispheric interactions in women while it is the intrahemispheric interactions that dominate in men. In a task of verbal production, PET also allowed Jaeger et al. (1998) to show a cerebral activation at the peri-sylvian level that was greater on the left in men and equivalent in both hemispheres in women. Nowicka and Fersten (2001) studied the time of transfer of information from one hemisphere to the other in a task of verbal treatment associated with words presented sometimes on the right visual hemifield and sometimes on the left visual hemifield. For this, they compared the latency of EP waves measured on both hemispheres. They showed, for this task, that the time of transfer from left to right is longer than the time of transfer from right to left in men, while in women these times of transfer are identical. The authors thus concluded a stronger lateralization in men. For our part (Fiori et al., 2001), in an experiment focusing on encoding of schematic faces (Mooney figures), we observed N170 at the infero-temopral level that was greater at the right than at the left in men, but equivalent amplitude on the two hemispheres in women (see Fig. 8.1). However, a result that is just as important is that in the study of Nowicka and Fersten (2001), as in ours, the behavioural performances of men and women were similar.

This dissociation between cerebral activation and behaviour may surprise, but it has been indicated by other authors and it is essential because it signifies that men and women (and, beyond that, probably all individuals) could adopt different strategies, including a more or less different prompting of the two hemispheres, to reach the same performance.

Finally, although certain anatomical differences seem to exist between the male and female brains, it is probably the functional differences that seem the most important.

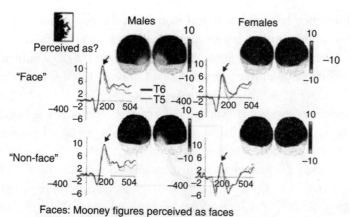

Faces: Mooney figures perceived as faces
Non-faces: Mooney figures not perceived as faces

The arrows indicate the peak of the N170 on the
right temporal electrode (T6) and the left temporal electrode (T5).

Fig. 8.1 Differences in cerebral activations between men and women during a task of face perception (Fiori et al., 2001). The subjects must indicate whether they perceive a face during the presentation of a Mooney figure right side up or upside down (only those results are presented here that correspond to the figures presented right side up). The N170 recorded on temporal electrodes are more ample at right (T6) than at left (T5) in men; they are equivalent on the two electrodes in women. The graphs of surface cerebral activities are established at the moment the N170 peaks.

$$\boxed{9}$$

Emotion and Cognition

We have already addressed in the preceding chapters some of the relationships that could exist between emotions and cognitive functions. For example, we have mentioned the role of prosody in the comprehension of language or relationships between recognition of facial expressions and facial recognition. For all that, it is necessary to observe that studies of emotions on the one hand and cognitive functions on the other have long ignored each other. In essence, it was considered that emotions, referring back to affectivity, belong to the realm of clinical psychology, while cognitive functions were somehow "emancipated" from the affective dimension and belonged to the field of "experimental" psychology. This dichotomy, relic of a cleavage between clinical psychology and behaviourism, is about to become history. The taking into account of underlying cerebral activities of cognitive functioning has contributed to this scientific evolution.

9.1   FROM STRESS TO VIGILANCE: THE BEGINNINGS

Hans Selye, a Canadian physiologist, introduced the concept of stress and gave it meaning in terms of the response of an organism to the disturbance of the homeostatic equilibrium, which leads to stimulation of any nature.

Selye defined stress as the non-specific response that the body gives to any demand that is made of it. This physiological response, called the general adaptation syndrome (Selye, 1956), comprises three stages: (1) alarm, during which the organism is disturbed and certain biological parameters are modified to prepare it for attack or defence (e.g., cardiac rhythm, arterial pressure); (2) adaptation, during which the organism is adapted to the disturbance by mobilizing its energy resources to master the situation; (3) possibly exhaustion, during which the adaptation to the situation has failed and the stage of alarm occurs again, which exhausts the organism's resources to the point of psychic and/or somatic pathology.[1]

Subsequently, Bloch (1966) proposed a model of vigilance in five levels located on a continuum, from sleep to hyperexcitation, through three intermediary levels (diffuse waking, attentive waking, emotion). These levels of vigilance are related with the level of activity of the nervous system and determine performance. At first, the performance increases to the extent that the level of vigilance increases, then it falls abruptly from a certain degree of activation of the nervous system: the curve expressing the relationship between performance and level of vigilance is thus an inverted U. To put it plainly, increase in the level of activity of the nervous system, and thus vigilance, is favourable only up to a point. Beyond that, the excess of vigilance is unfavourable for performance[2] (measured by reaction time). There is thus an "optimum" level of vigilance for which performance is maximal: below and above this optimum of vigilance, the performance is lower. Bloch precisely located this inversion of the link between level of vigilance and level of performance at the beginning of the fourth stage, that of emotion, which when it comes into play degrades performance. Indeed, this is a conception of emotion in terms of stress. It is known today that the effects of stress, the emotional reactions with which it is associated, are more complex because, notably, they depend on the interpretation of the situation by the individual who lives through it, of exogenous factors as well as endogenous factors (Mandler, 1984). Thus, a particular event may exercise a constraint on some individuals and not on others. This is the case, for

---

[1] The film *Mon Oncle d'Amérique*, by A. Resnais, in which Henri Laborit explains the effects of situations in which the character played by Gerard Depardieu finds himself in terms of experiments carried out on rats, clearly illustrates these physiological reactions.

[2] This phenomenon is frequently observed in common life: one "feels" hyperexcited, one is perfectly awake, and still one fails in certain actions (e.g., dropping an object seized in a hurry).

example, demonstrated by ergonomists in work situations, of a single task that has to be achieved by a novice—the task could thus be a source of stress—and by an expert. Moreover, for a single individual, what might be a source of stress at one moment may not be so at another. A source of noise may constitute a source of stress in a working condition. On the contrary, in a rest situation, it may not be noticed, or may even be noticed as being agreeable. Numerous studies have thus been carried out on the effects of noise on performance and have given rise to contradictory data; the same noise could result in improvement of or on the contrary degradation of performance. In reality, the inconsistency of these data is only apparent and could be removed if one takes into account the task in which the subject is engaged as well as his or her internal state (in terms of level of vigilance, notably). The noise increases the level of vigilance, and its effect may be beneficial or on the contrary harmful to the performance of the subject, depending on whether the subject's level of vigilance is below the optimum level or has already been reached. The stress, a source of arousal and mobilization of resources, can thus have a positive effect, as observed all the time, for example, in actors who have stage fright before entering a scene and then give the best of themselves thanks to the resources that they nevertheless mobilize. But we know well that fear can on the contrary paralyse us and prevent us from acting, as for example in the case of a student whose mind goes blank during an exam.

From these few examples, one anticipates the possible links between emotion and attention, and emotion and memory. Although the theoretical trend integrating emotions with cognitive activity dates only from the first hypothesis of Mandler (1984), it is presently much more active and strongly influenced by the studies of Damasio (1994).

9.2 THE MECHANISMS OF EMOTIONS

Before further studying the link between cognition and emotion, it is necessary to explain the basic concepts of emotion and the mechanisms and circuits that underlie it.

9.2.1 Definitions

Neurobiologists distinguish emotion as a subjective sentiment—the emotion that one "feels"—of physiological arousal that it provokes with its procession of somatic reactions and associated actions (e.g., defence or attack when faced with danger). This last aspect flows directly from Darwinian theory, according to which emotion plays an essential role in the survival of organisms. It may be noted that only subjective sentiment is peculiar to humans.

Historically, among neurobiologists, there are several successive theoretical currents that put the accent on various aspects of emotions: (a) perception of physiological events that are associated with them (theory of James, 1884 and Lange, 1887), (b) the central processes of cerebral integration of emotional experience and emotive reaction (theory of Cannon, 1927), and (c) cognitive interpretation in terms of emotion of corporeal states (theory of Schachter, 1964).

In psychology, the tendency is to distinguish a set of fundamental emotions on which are grafted more varied and nuanced emotions, the debate focusing on the definition of basic emotions. In the first place (since Wundt in the 19th century), the three fundamental pairs of emotions were pleasure/displeasure, tension/release, excitation/relaxation, but this list has gradually been enriched and refined. For example, studying the recognition of facial expressions, Ekman and Friesen (1978, 1986) proposed a list of basic facial expressions comprising joy, fear, anger, surprise, sadness, disgust and contempt. Nevertheless, the literature on the subject may cause confusion in the recognition of certain emotions, such as between surprise and joy, surprise and fear, anger and disgust. Moreover, the expression of an emotion by the face is expressed in a variable social and cultural context depending on the individuals, social codes, etc. In conclusion, the list of basic emotions remains debatable, as does their manifestation in the face, which also expresses other functions.

In any case, the question of a link between emotional sentiment and on the one hand physiological activity, and on the other hand cerebral activities, remains an essential question.

9.2.2 The Circuits of Emotions

It is known from experience that emotional "sentiment" often accompanies physiological reactions (acceleration of heartbeat, blushing, etc.) that constitute responses of the autonomous nervous system. But this is not always the case. Moreover, these physiological reactions are not specific to a particular emotion. One can as well feel one's heart beat faster on the arrival of a train from which a loved one will alight as when one feels a great fear or anger. Moreover, these physiological reactions are also present in situations *a priori* devoid of emotion (e.g., an illness with high fever). Observing this, the celebrated physiologist Cannon propounded, in 1927, his theory according to which emotion felt is not the consequence of physiological changes and that in consequence emotional experience can intervene independently of emotional expression. According to the theory of Cannon, it is the thalamus that, receiving the sensory messages and cortical messages, plays the essential role in the determination of the character of emotion.

(a) *The Papez circuit*

Towards 1930, Papez suggested a "system of emotion" linking the cortex to the hypothalamus, commonly designated the "Papez circuit" located on the medial wall of the brain. Already mentioned in the preceding chapters, this circuit ensures communication in both directions between the cortex and the hypothalamus. The cingular cortex sends efferences to the hippocampus, which acts on the hypothalamus by the fornix (a network of efferent fibres of the hippocampus). The hypothalamus acts on the cingular cortex by its efferent pathway, which passes through the anterior nuclei of the thalamus. Finally, the cingular cortex itself communicates—in both directions—with the neocortex.

According to Papez, this circuit is the basis of emotional life while the expression of emotions depends on a control exerted by the hypothalamus on the visceral organs. For memory, recall that this region was in 1878 called the "limbic lobe" (from the Latin *limbus*, edge) by Broca, who thus designated the cortex located on the medial face of the temporal lobe, comprising the hippocampus, the cingular gyrus, and portion of cortex surrounding the callous body. Since the "three brain" theory of McLean (1955), this region is called the "limbic system" and, according to McLean, constitutes the second "brain",[3] appearing during the course of evolution and implicated in the survival of the individual in bringing forth adapted visceral and affective responses. Still, it is known that the theory of McLean according to which the limbic system is the "brain of emotions" is today rejected insofar as later studies showed that some of these structures—the hippocampus for example—do not intervene in emotions, whereas others— at the level of the cerebral trunk notably—are highly implicated in the visceral reactions characteristic of emotions.

(b) *The Klüver-Bucy syndrome*

During an experiment carried out on apes, Klüver and Bucy (1939), having carried out bilateral ablation of temporal lobes (including the hippocampus

---

[3] According to McLean, the brain evolved in three "layers" from the least evolved to the most evolved, with, from the interior to the exterior: the reptilian brain, the palaeo-mammalian brain (palaeocortex) and the neomammalian brain (neocortex). The three brains cohabit only in the most evolved species.

and the amygdala and an important part of the temporal neocortex), observed that the animals thus operated on presented a set of significant problems, including modification of sexual behaviour in males that manifests itself in hypersexuality, tendency to put things in their mouths and to eat unusual foods, or more precisely all sorts of objects that are not food, as well as a total loss of reactions of anger and fear with respect to stimuli triggering these reactions in healthy animals. This experiment was the first to show the intervention of a cerebral region in emotional processes.

Later studies in animals as well as observation of patients have made it possible to hypothesize that, among the structures of the temporal lobe involved in ablation carried out in the preceding experiment, it was probably the absence of the *amygdala*, consecutive to the lesion, that played the essential role in the emotional reduction observed. This hypothesis was supported by the case of SM, a patient of Adolphs et al. (1994). SM was a rare case of specific bilateral lesion of the amygdala. This patient had difficulty in recognizing facial expressions. Although she could recognize joy, sadness and disgust, she could not recognize fear.

(c) *The amygdala and its connections: fear and aggressiveness*

The amygdala—a small almond-shaped structure located in the infero-medial part of the temporal lobe at the end of the hippocampus—is in fact a set of small nuclei: the basolateral nuclei, the cortico-medial nuclei, the central nucleus (the names of these various nuclei differ slightly according to the authors). Because of this large number of nuclei, some authors talk moreover of the *amygdalian complex*. These nuclei are themselves so closely interconnected that the information that reaches one is transmitted to the others. Thus, it is thought that the lateral nucleus constitutes the pathway of entry of the amygdala but that the information that reaches it is then transmitted to the baso-lateral nuclei and the central nucleus, which constitutes the "exit door" from the amygdala.

The connections of the amygdala are numerous and generally bidirectional (a single structure sends information to the amygdala and receives it in turn). The amygdala is thus primarily a site of convergence of information.

In the first place, it receives sensory information on the one hand from the sensory cortex and on the other from the thalamus (recall that the thalamus is a relay on the sensory pathways, upstream of the cortex). The pathway issuing directly from the thalamus is a subcortical pathway; it is thus rapid. It projects to the ventral nucleus of the amygdala and makes possible an immediate perception of the situation and the immediate triggering of emotional reactions. This "rapid pathway" probably thus serves as an alert in case of immediate danger. The pathway from the cortex is a slower pathway. From the sensory organs, it transits by the thalamus and then the sensory cortex. This gives first of all a complete representation of the stimulus— which supposes a passage through the primary cortex and the unimodal associative cortex. Then, the passage through the multimodal associative cortex also allows us to assess the entire situation. Thus, after the immediate reaction triggered by the rapid pathway, the information transiting through the slow pathway makes it possible then to "correct" this reaction, if needed, by assessing whether the stimulus perceived by the rapid pathway actually constitutes a danger.

The amygdala also receives information from the hippocampus. One sees often that the latter is implicated in the formation of explicit memory. This pathway could thus be the source of the triggering of an emotion from a memory and from a stimulus evoking a memory that is emotionally charged. Generally, the intervention of the hippocampus on the amygdala makes it possible to place the present situation in a context.

The amygdala is also connected with subcortical structures: septum, hypothalamus, and reticulate formation of the cerebral trunk.

The efferences of the amygdala are also numerous. It sends projections to all the structures that send projections to it. In particular, the stria terminalis pathway is an important efferent pathway of the amygdala that projects to the subcortical structures the septum and hypothalamus.

Finally, it is connected with the frontal lobe and more particularly with the prefrontal cortex.

Experiments of conditioning in animals, descriptions of patients, and experiments in human brain imaging tend to show that the amygdala plays an essential role in the learning of fear and in the reactions of aggressiveness. For example, Kapp et al. (1984) conditioned rabbits to associate a sound with pain following an electric shock (another sound was "neutral": it was not associated with such a shock). The authors then observed reactions of fear (increase in cardiac rate) when they delivered the sound associated with the electric shock, while these reactions were not developed with the neutral stimulus. Having recorded the response of neurons of the amygdala over the course of this experimental situation, they observed that these did not respond to sounds before the conditioning but afterwards they responded to the sound associated with the electric shock and only to that sound.

An experiment of the same type was carried out in fMRI in humans (La Bar et al., 1998) with conditioning of subjects to fear by a mild electric shock associated with the presentation of certain visual images. The authors observed an increase in the activation of the amygdala for the stimuli triggering fear, associated with the activation of cortical regions, including the cingular cortex.

In some epileptic patients in which electrodes were implanted in various structures of the temporal lobe in order to identify the seat of epilepsy, it was observed (Bancaud et al., 1994) that the stimulation of the amygdala was associated with a sentiment of fear. Note that, most of the time, patients in which the epileptic site is located in the temporal lobe describe an intense sensation of fear immediately before the epileptic crisis. Similarly, patients who have undergone destruction of the amygdala following a cerebral vascular accident no longer recognize the expression of fear on a face, while they remain capable of recognizing other facial expressions.

The amygdala thus seems to be "at the centre" of implicated circuits, notably, in the perception of danger and triggering of responses necessary to fight this danger or to flee it. These reactions that imply movements (to flee or fight) are probably made possible by connections that also support the amygdala with basal ganglia, implicated in the control of movement.

(d) *The meso-cortico-limbic network and the pleasure-compensation system*
In 1954, Olds and Milner refined an experimental paradigm of self-stimulation in the rat. Their experiment made it possible to discover the existence of two antagonistic systems of pleasure-compensation and aversion-punishment.

In the first experiment of Olds and Milner, the rats in which the authors implanted an electrode of stimulation in the brain (in the septal area more precisely during the very first experiment) were placed in a conditioning cage. When they passed into a certain place in this cage, the experimenters delivered to them a stimulation through the implanted electrode. In fact, very soon, the rats remained in this place in the cage. Then, the authors placed a pedal in the cage such that the stimulation was delivered only when the rat remained on the pedal. The rats very quickly learned to press the pedal to self-stimulate. The most astonishing thing in the experiment was that the rats pressed incessantly on the pedal, neglecting to eat and drink, until they were exhausted. Moreover, placed in a complex maze, they learned very quickly to discover the pedal that allowed them to auto-stimulate and this even if a very violent electric shock was then delivered to them. The hypothesis of a search for pleasure and of the cerebral structures implicated in this research was thus proposed. Several cerebral structures have thus been tested by modifying the site of implantation of the electrode. The same type of self-stimulation behaviour has been observed for the entire middle bundle of the telencephalus, from the ventral tegmental area in the cerebral trunk to the frontal cortex projecting to various subcortical structures. In these conditions, the hypothesis has been advanced that the structures giving rise to self-stimulation constitute "pleasure centres". At least, it seems that the stimulation of structures of the middle bundle of the telencephalus provokes an effect of compensation, probably that which is the basis of reinforcement of Pavlovian conditioning.

Similar observations were made in humans on two patients (a narcoleptic patient and an epileptic patient) in which electrodes were implanted to identify the sites responsible for their pathology. The sensations reported by these patients—satisfaction, pleasure, exhilaration, or on the contrary irritation—when the various cerebral regions were stimulated are entirely consistent with the observations made in the preceding experiment in rats.

Finally, we may speak of a "pleasure" system—what the behaviourists call the circuit of positive reinforcement or compensation—including the ventral tegmental area, the nucleus accumbens, the septum, the amygdala, the prefrontal cortex, and certain regions of the thalamus (see Fig. 9.1).

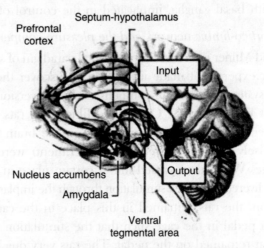

Fig. 9.1 The "pleasure-compensation" system. The arrows indicate the direction of information circulation between the different structures involved, from sensory inputs (input) by which stimuli are perceived to motor outputs (output) that carry the motor responses, passing through the prefrontal cortex, nucleus accumbens, amygdala, septum, and ventral tegmental area.

Here it is a network composed of two pathways: the meso-limbic pathway that starts from the mesencephalus and projects to the nucleus accumbens (or ventral striatum, located in the septal region) and the meso-cortical pathway that projects to the frontal cortex. All these structures are interconnected with the lateral nucleus and or the ventromedial nucleus of the hypothalamus, which retroacts on the ventral tegmental area and on the vegetative functions as well as on the endocrine functions by the intermediary of the hypophysis.

It is interesting to note that the functioning of the meso-cortico-limbic network relies on the intervention of specific neurotransmitters, the primary one being dopamine: this network is called the dopaminergic pathway. Several studies on drug dependence implicate dopaminergic receptors as a point of convergence of actions of various drugs even if the drugs in the first stage act on other neurotransmitters. Thus, amphetamines and cocaine activate the dopaminergic neurons: amphetamines directly stimulate dopamine release, while cocaine inhibits its recapture by presynaptic neurons. Other drugs (e.g., alcohol) hinder the activity of GABA interneurons of the ventral tegmental area and of the nucleus accumbens. The normal function of these GABA interneurons is to inhibit the dopaminergic neurons of these two regions. Alcohol thus acts to block the inhibiting action of these interneurons, which release the action of dopaminergic neurons and the liberation of dopamine. To conclude on this link between addictions and the dopaminergic pathway, we can finally cite the existence of nicotinic receptors on dopaminergic neurons of the mesencephalus, which, when they are activated, augment the presynaptic liberation of dopamine. Thus, the role of dopamine in the compensation-pleasure system is established, even if the mechanism of its intervention is not yet clearly known.[4]

9.3 EMOTION AND COGNITION

Beyond "basic" emotional reactions described earlier, it seems that the link between emotion and cognition is increasingly advanced in the literature: the emotions are under cognitive control at the same time as they influence cognitive treatments.

9.3.1 The Role of the Prefrontal Cortex

Recall first of all that the frontal lobe extends from the Rolando fissure to the Sylvian fissure and comprises the following regions: the posterior part is devoted to the motor areas (located just before the Rolando fissure or the central fissure) and premotor areas (comprising notably Broca's area); the prefrontal region, before the preceding, which comprises the dorso-lateral

---

[4] We must also mention the fact that the stimulation of the septum of the medial bundle of the telencephalus leads to the liberation of endorphins (endogenous morphines) at the level of the ventral tegmental area.

cortex, the medial cortex and the orbital part; and finally the paralimbic cortex comprising the posterior orbito-frontal cortex and the cingular gyrus located on the inner surface of the hemispheres.

Relying on case studies of his patients, Damasio (1994) showed that the cerebral circuits of emotions are not limited to the limbic system and extend to the prefrontal cortex. Damasio thus reanalyzed, a posteriori, the case of Phineas Gage, a famous patient, reported initially by his doctor, John Harlow. In 1848, during an explosion on a railway line construction site, Gage, the site supervisor, was hit in the face with by an iron rod of 3 cm diameter weighing 10 kg, which penetrated his face at the left cheek, and emerged at the top of the head, after having crossed the anterior part of his brain. Curiously, Gage survived but his behaviour and his personality were profoundly changed. He became rough, disrespectful, stubborn, no longer tolerating restrictions or advice. In short, as Damasio reported, his character, his tastes and antipathies, his dreams and ambitions changed totally. At the time, the description of this patient by Harlow himself did not rouse much scientific interest. But in the scientific context of that time, it was inconceivable that "reason" could be thus assigned to a particular region of the brain. Moreover, the precise description of the lesion was lacking, unlike in the cases of patients of Broca and Wernicke dating from the same period. Finally, precisely, the case of aphasia described by Broca had a lesion of the left frontal lobe, while he presented no behavioural problems: obviously, Gage also was affected in the left frontal lobe according to Harlow's description and was not aphasic.

Another case, that of Elliot, a patient of Damasio, made it possible to refine Damasio's theses on the role of the prefrontal region. Elliot was affected with a cerebral tumor that ran along the middle line of the brain, above the nasal cavities, at the region located above the summit of the eye-sockets, which compressed the adjacent cerebral tissue in the two frontal lobes. After ablation of the tumour, Elliot's personality also changed: an intelligent man, he could perform many tasks in isolation, as before, but on the other hand he was no longer capable of planning his activities over the short or long term or to respect orders or times; he was ruined in his financial speculations—a behaviour that he had never had beforehand. Very quickly, it became clear that this behaviour showed pathology and not a simple circumstantial "slip" or an anterior character trait. All the conventional psychological and neuropsychological tests carried out in the laboratory revealed that Elliot still had an above-average intelligence and that his perceptive capacities, his short-term and long-term memory, and his aptitude for learning, speaking and calculating remained intact, as well as his capacity to focus attention on a particular object or his capacities of working memory. On the other hand, Damasio remarked that Elliot, while remaining very polite and respectful, had an ironic air, slightly condescending, cold and distant, and that he did not seem affected when discussing his problems, including his most intimate difficulties, which would have embarrassed any other person. Elliot recounted his "adventure" with a total detachment and without apparent emotion. Damasio, suspecting an emotional problem, presented him with images that normally evoked strong emotional reactions (burning houses, bloody accidents) and observed that Elliot did not feel positive or negative emotion at seeing such images. Thus, Damasio came to hypothesize that Elliot was capable of knowing but not feeling and that the reduction of his emotional capacities was the basis of the reduction of his rational apprehension of situations, including his own. The scanners and MRI allowed Damasio to locate Elliot's lesions: the orbital region and medial region of the two frontal lobes as well as, in the right frontal lobe, the white matter located under the cerebral cortex to the extent that a large part of the right prefrontal cortex was no longer functional. On the other hand, neither the motor and premotor areas nor Broca's area and neighbouring regions, nor the bases of the telencephalus, nor the other cerebral regions were damaged. As in the case of Gage, the damaged region pertained to the ventromedial portion of the prefrontal cortex and was more extensive at the right than at the left.

The cases of Gage and Elliot emphasized the role of the frontal lobes and, more precisely, of the prefrontal region, in the adaptation of behaviour to the social environment. For Damasio, the weakening of the capacity to react emotionally could be the source of irrational behaviour. Our acts are thus dictated as much by their objective finality as by their possible personal and social consequences.

9.3.2 The Theory of Somatic Markers

Following his observations of numerous patients affected by prefrontal lesions, Damasio elaborated the theory of somatic markers.

To understand it, it is important to recall the connections between the prefrontal cortex (notably its ventromedial part, corresponding to Brodmann areas 10, 11, 12, 13, 25) with the structures of the limbic system, the role of which in emotions we saw earlier. These linkages between the associative areas of the prefrontal cortex and the limbic system—and beyond that the vegetative system—are thus the basis of the link between rationality and emotions that, for Damasio, did not reveal separate functions: on the contrary, reasoning and the decision-making to which reasoning leads would be guided by their predictable consequences in terms of satisfaction or on the contrary dissatisfaction. The "error of Descartes" is, according to him, to have separated "cartesian" reasoning from emotions and passions. It is not in our brief to enter here into the debate whether this is effectively the position of Descartes: many authors emphasize that this is a false debate, even a groundless accusation against Descartes by Damasio.[5] This link between rationality and emotions is ensured by the orbito-frontal cortex that links the associative areas of the prefrontal cortex to the limbic system. The somatic markers are, for the author of this theory, traces of pleasant or unpleasant situations, in other terms emotions, forged during similar anterior situations, even of genetic origin for some of them. These markers constitute affective memories that allow us to test various options of a situation: automatically and unconsciously, we anticipate the possible consequences of these various options and could inhibit the choices marked negatively in favour of choices marked positively. The somatic markers are thus acquired during the course of our experiences and vegetative reactions that lead from them.

Experiments proving this hypothesis of somatic markers "guiding" cognition are still in their infancy. Some of them use the electrodermal response (EDR) as an indicator of somatic markers. This index is based on skin conductance: if one places an electrode on the palm of the hand, the skin conducts more or less current through this electrode and will conduct better if the skin is moist. The stress (more generally any stimulus) causes a reaction of the vegetative system that manifests itself in mild sweating. This technique is the "lie detector" technique: a person who reveals an EDR when he or she responds to a question is considered to have lied (the stress generated by the lie leads to the EDR). Precisely speaking, however, the EDR is a non-specific indicator: any stimulus is in itself stressful—and the fact even of being subjected to this test is a stressful situation—it is very easy to obtain an EDR and this has no significance other than that there is a vegetative reaction to a stress agent. Because of this non-specific character of EDR—and derivates such as its use as a lie detector—this method has been abandoned in research. Nevertheless, it is perfectly suitable for situations in which one needs only an index of vegetative reaction. For this reason, it is suitable for research about somatic markers of emotions.

Several researchers have thus carried out studies in collaboration with Damasio using this index. Bechara et al. (1999) first showed that patients with lesions in the ventromedial prefrontal cortex did not present variations

---

[5] Recall all the same that Descartes was the author of *Traité des Passions*.

of EDR (unlike control subjects) when they were shown emotional images (e.g., mutilated or "naked" bodies) or when asked to remember joyous or sad events (e.g., wedding or burials). Moreover, even when they were perfectly capable of describing these memories, if they were asked to attribute an emotional value to them, the subjective evaluation that they made did not differ from that attributed to "neutral" events. This result posed, the researchers (Bechara et al., 2000) subjected the same type of patients (and the control subjects) to a task that they called the "gambling task", which combined uncertainty, reward and penalties. The subjects received a fictitious sum of money that they were expected to multiply. They drew cards that could lead to a gain or a loss but the gains and losses with cards from piles A and B were greater than those from piles B and C. The control subjects gradually learned that the losses that they could undergo in drawing a card from pile A or B constituted a long-term risk much greater than the gains associated with these two piles: thus, very quickly, they drew cards only from pile C or D. The brain-damaged patients affected in the ventromedial cortex did not exhibit this behaviour and continued to draw from piles C and D till the end despite the losses they suffered, which showed their inability to anticipate possible losses. But the most remarkable part of this experiment pertained to data relative to the EDR. At the beginning of the experiment, the patients, like the controls showed an increase in their EDR when they drew a card. As the experiment progressed, the control subjects showed an EDR *before* drawing a card, which seemed thus to display an anticipatory vegetative reaction. On the contrary, in the patients, this EDR never became anticipatory. The authors concluded that in these patients there was no sign of the influence of emotion on their decisions.

For the present, the hypothesis of somatic markers remains a hypothesis. In any case, one must note that it is complementary to the phenomenon of long-term potentiation described in Chapter 5, in which a long-term modification of synapses marks the phenomenon of memorization. Thus, it is possible that neuronal activation caused by emotional reactions during an event added to that caused by the event itself, leading to a long-term potentiation, favours the memorizing of this event, thus explaining the common observation that one memorizes facts better when they are associated with a strong emotion.

9.3.3 Emotion and Attention

Recall the case of SM, studied by Adolphs et al. (1994), suggesting a specific role of the amygdala in recognition of fear. Ten years later, the same team

(Adlophs et al., 2005) demonstrated that this deficit of recognition of fear in SM probably came from an incapacity to focus on the region of the eyes, a trait most important for recognizing fear. According to them, although other facial emotions can be recognized from other traits, the eyes are necessary for recognition of fear. They showed that, when the instructor insisted on the patient's need to watch the eyes, SM recovered his capacity to recognize fear. They thus returned to their interpretation of specific deficit of recognition of fear in SM. This deficiency observed in SM comes in fact from the difficulty of focusing on the region of the eyes. The specific role of the amygdala concerns the treatment of visual information of the eye region because the amygdala exerts control over visual areas. Recall that the connections between the amygdala and the areas of the visual cortex are so bidirectional that the amygdala sends information to visual areas (at the same time, of course, that it receives information from them). By that means the amygdala, according to the authors, participates in the control of attention directed towards the eye region.

Other recent works, based on fMRI (Vuilleumier et al., 2003), showed that the response of the amygdala to facial expressions of fear was important when the photos of faces were filtered so as to leave only the low frequencies (fluid images with poorly visible traits) while it was weaker when the photos were filtered on high frequencies (apparent traits). In the case of activation of the amygdala by photos filtered by low frequencies, an activation of superior colliculi and pulvinar was also observed, which suggests that there is activation of a very rapid subcortical pathway, based on information from the magnocellular pathway, short-circuiting the slowest pathway passing through the cortex (which itself relies on information from the ventral parvocellular pathway). This subcortical pathway allows very rapid categorization of emotional stimuli by the amygdala. Beyond their complexity, these data show on the one hand that the treatment of emotions is based on the complex perceptive and attentional processes implicating various cortical and subcortical neuronal networks and on the other hand that emotion cannot be disconnected from cognition.

In conclusion, studies tending to prove a link between emotion and cognitive functions are at present increasingly numerous. Moreover, if we distinguish different regions within the prefrontal cortex, there remains the fact that the dorso-lateral cortex, the ventromedial cortex, and the cingular cortex constitute probably a complex network at the base of this link between emotion and cognition.

References

Aboitiz F., Scheibel A.B. and Zaidel E. (1992). Morphometry of the Sylvian fissure and the corpus callosum with emphasis on sex difference. *Brain*, **115**: 1521-1541.

Adolphs R., Damasio H. and Damasio A. (1994). Impaired recognition of emotion in facial expressions following bilateral damage to the human amygdala. *Nature*, **372**, 669: 672.

Adolphs R., Tranel D., Hamann S., Young A., Calder A.J., Phelps E.A., *et al.* (1999). Recognition of facial emotion in nine individuals with bilateral amygdala damage. *Neuropsychologia*, **37**: 1111-1117.

Adolphs R., Gosselin F., Buchanan T.W., Tranel D., Schyns P. and Damasio A. (2005). A mechanism for impaired fear recognition after amygdala damage. *Nature*, **433**, 68: 72.

Allen G., Buxton R.B., Wong E.C. and Courchesne E. (1997). Attentional activation of cerebellum independent of motor involvement. *Science*, **275 (5308)**: 1940-1943.

Allen L.S. and Gorski R.A. (1991). Sexual dimorphism of the anterior commissure and massa intermedia of the human brain. *Journal of Comparative Neurology*, **312**: 97-104.

Allen L.S., Rishley M.E., Chai Y.M. and Gorski R.A. (1991). Sex differences in the corpus callosum of the living human being. *Journal of Neuroscience*, **11**: 933-942.

Atkinson R.C. and Shiffrin R.M. (1968). Human memory: A proposed system and its control processes. In: K.W. Spence and J.T. Spence (Eds.), *The Psychology of Learning and Motivation*, vol. 2: 89-195. New York: Academic Press.

Azzari N.P., Pettigrew K.D., Pietrini P., Murphy D.G., Horwitz B. and Schapiro M.B. (1995). Sex differences in patterns of hemispheric cerebral metabolism: a multiple regression/discriminant analysis of positron emission tomographic data. *International Journal of Neuroscience*, **81(1-2)**: 1-20.

Baddeley A. and Hitch G. (1974). Working memory. In: G.H. Bower (Ed.), *The Psychology of Learning and Memory*, vol. 8: 47-89. New York: Academic Press.

Bagot J.-D. (1999). *Information, Sensation et Perception*. Paris: Armand Colin, coll. "Cursus".

Bancaud J., Brunet-Bougin F., Chauvel P. and Halgren E. (1994). Anatomical origin of "déjà vu" and vivid "memories" in human temporal lobes. *Brain*, 117: 71-90.

Bechara A., Damasio H., Damasio A.R. and Lee G.P. (1999). Different contributions of the human amygdala and ventromédial prefrontal cortex to decision-making. *The Journal of Neuroscience*, **19**: 5473-5481.

Bechara A., Damasio H. and Damasio A.R. (2000). Emotion, decision making and the orbitofrontal cortex. *Cerebral Cortex*, **10**: 295-307.

Benedict R.H., Lockwood A.H., Shucard J.L., Shucard D.W., Wack D. and Murphy B.W. (1998). Functional neuroimaging of attention in the auditory modality. *NeuroReport*, **9(1)**: 121-126.

Bentin S., Allison T., Puce A., Perez E. and McCarthy G. (1996). Electrophysiological studies of face perception in humans. *Journal of Cognitive Neuroscience*, **8**: 551-565.

Benton A.L. and Van Allen M.W. (1973). *Test of Facial Recognition*, Publication n° 287, Neurosensory Center (University of Iowa, Ames, Iowa).

Biederman I. (1972). Perceiving real-world scenes. *Science*, **177**: 77-80.

Bliss T.V. and Lomo T. (1973). Long-lasting potentiation of synaptic transmission in the dentate area of the anaesthetized rabbit following stimulation of the perforant path. *Journal of Physiology* (London), 232: 331-356.

Bloch V. (1966). Les niveaux de vigilance. In: *Traité de Psychologie Expérimentale, III, Psychophysiologie du Comportement*, P. Fraisse et J. Piaget dir., PUF, Paris.

Bötzel K. and Grüsser O.J. (1989). Electric brain potentials evoked by pictures of faces and non-faces: a search for "face-specific" EEG potentials. *Experimental Brain Research*, **77**: 349-360.

Bötzel K., Grüsser O.J., Häussler B. and Naumann A. (1989). The search for face-specific evoked potentials. In: E. Basar and T.H. Bullock (Eds.), *Springer Series in Brain Dynamics*, vol. 2: 449-466. Berlin: Springer-Verlag.

Broadbent D. (1958). *Perception and Communication*. London: Pergamon Press.

Broadbent D.E. (1970). Stimulus set and response set. In: D.I. Mortofsky (Ed.), *Attention: Contemporary Theories and Analysis*. New York: Appleton-Century-Crofts.

Bruce V. and Young A. (1986). Understanding face recognition. *British Journal of Psychology*, **77**: 305-327.

Bruyer R. (1983). *Le Visage et l'Expression Faciale: Approche Neuropsychologique*. Brussels: Mardaga.

Bruyer R. (1987). *Les Mécanismes de la Reconnaissance des Visages*. Grenoble: Presses Universitaires de Grenoble.

Cabezza R. and Nyberg L. (2000). Imaging cognition II: an empirical review of 275 PET and fRMI studies. *Journal of Cognitive Neurosciences*, **12: 1**, 1-47.

Cannon W.B. (1927). The James-Lange theory of emotion: a critical examination and an alternative theory. *American Journal of Psychology*, **39**: 106-124.

Chiarello C. (1991). Interpretation of word meanings by the cerebral hemispheres. In: R.J. Schwahenflugel (Ed.), *The Psychology of Word Meanings*, Hillsdale, N.J.: Lawrence Erlbaum Associates.

Clark V.P., Parasuraman R., Keil K., Kulansky R., Fannon S., Maisog J.M., Ungerleider L.G. and Haxby J.V. (1997). Selective attention to face identity and color studied with fRMI. *Human Brain Mapping*, **5**: 293-297.

Collins A.M. and Loftus E.E. (1975). A spreading-activation theory of semantic processing. *Psychological Review*, 82: 407-428.

Corbetta M. and Shulman G.L. (2002). Control of goal-directed and stimulus-driven attention in the brain. *Nature Reviews Neuroscience*, **3**: 201-215.

Corbetta M., Miezin F.M., Dobmeyer S., Shulman G.L. and Petersen S.E. (1990). Attentional modulation of neural processing of shape, color and velocity in humans. *Science*, **248(4962)**: 1556-1559.

Corbetta M., Shulman G.L., Miezin F.M. and Petersen S.E. (1993). A PET study of visuospatial attention. *Journal of Neuroscience*, **13(3)**: 1202-1226.

Corbetta M., Kincade J.M., Ollinger J.-M., McAvoy M.P. and Shulman G.L. (2000). Voluntary orienting is dissociated from target detection in human posterior parietal cortex. *Nature Neurosciences*, **3 (3)**: 292-297.

Corsi-Cabrera M., Herrera P. and Malvido M. (1989). Correlation between EEG and cognitive abilities: sex differences. *International Journal of Neurosciences*, **45(1-2)**: 133-141.

Corsi-Cabrera M., Arce C., Ramos J. and Guevara M.A. (1997). Effect of spatial ability and sex on inter- and intrahemispheric correlation of EEG activity. *EEG and Clinical Neurophysiology*, **102(1)**: 5-11.

Coull J.T. and Nobre A.C. (1998). Where and when to pay attention: the neural systems for directing attention to spatial locations and to time intervals, as revealed by both PET and fRMI. *The Journal of Neurosciences*, **18**: 7426-7435.

Courtney S.M., Ungerleider L.G., Kell K. and Haxby V. (1997). Transient and sustained activity in a distributed neural system for human working memory. *Science*, **386**: 608-611.

Dabbs J.M. Jr, Chang E.L., Strong R.A. and Milun R. (1998). Spatial ability, navigation strategy and geographic knowledge among men and women. *Evolution and Human Behavior*, **19(2)**: 89-98.

Damasio A. (1994). *Descartes' error. Emotion, reason and the human brain.* Brosset/Putman Books. *Traduction française* (1995): *L'erreur de Descartes.* Odile Jacob, Paris, 368 p.

Damasio A. and Damasio H. (1992). Le cerveau et le Langage. *Pour la Science*, **1818**.

Damasio H., Grabowski T.J., Hichwa R.D. and Da masio A.R. (1996). A neural basis for lexical retrieval. *Nature*, **380(6574)**: 499-505.

Davidoff J. (1986). The specificity of face perception: evidence from psychological investigations. In: R. Bruyer (Ed.), *The Neuropsychology of Face Perception and Facial Expression*, pp. 147-166. London: Erlabaum.

Davidoff J. and Donelly N. (1990). Object superiority: a comparison of complete and part probes. *Acta Psychologica*, **73**: 225-243.

Dawson D.G. (1951). A summation technique for detecting small signals in a large irregular background. *Journal of Physiology*, **494**: 251-262.

De Renzi (1986). Current issues on prosopagnosia. In: H.D. Ellis, M.A. Jeeves, F.G. Nexcombe and A. Young (Eds.), *Aspects of Face Processing*, pp. 243-252, Dordrecht: Martinus Nijhoff.

Desgranges B., Bernard F. and Eustache F. (2003). La distinction épisodique/ sémantique et l'organisation catégorielle de la mémoire sémantique: données de l'imagerie cérébrale fonctionnelle. *Revue de Neuropsychologie*, **13(1)**: 115-162.

Desimone R., Albright T.D., Gross C.G. and Bruce C. (1984). Stimulus-selective properties of inferior temporal neurons in the macaque. *The Journal of Neurosciences*, **4(8)**: 2051-2062.

Deutsch J. and Deutsch D. (1963). Attention: Some theoretical considerations. *Psychological Review*, **70**: 80-90.

Donchin E. (1981). Surprise!.... Surprise? *Psychophysiology*, **18**: 493-515.

Eichenbaum H., Fagan H., Mathews P. and Cohen N.J. (1988). Hippocampal system dysfunction and odor discrimination learning in rats: impairment or facilitation depending on representational demands. *Behavioral Neuroscience*, **102**: 331-339.

Ekman P. and Friesen W.V. (1978). *Facial Action Coding System: Investigator's Guide*. Palo Alto: Consulting Psychologists Press.

Ekman P. and Friesen W.V. (1986). A new pan-cultural expression of emotion. *Motivation and Emotion*, **10**: 159-168.

Farah M.J. (1990). *Visual Agnosia*. Cambridge, Mass.: MIT Press.

Farah M.J. (1994). Specialization within visual object recognition: clues from prosopagnosia and alexia. In: M.J. Farah and G. Ratcliff (Eds.), *The Neuropsychology of High-Level Vision*, pp. 133-146. Hillsdale: Lawrence Erlbaum Associates.

Fiori N., Chaby L. and George N. (2001). Gender differences in the neural bases of face processing and recognition: two ERP studies. In: N. Fiori, M.H. Giard and B. Renault (Eds.), *International Journal of Psychophysiology*, **41(3)**.

Fize, Boulanouar, Chatel, Ranjeva, Fabre-Thorpe and Thorpe. (2000). Brain areas involved in rapid categorization of natural images: an event-related fRMI study. *NeuroImage*, **11**: 634-643.

Fodor J.A. (1983). *The Modularity of the Mind: An Essay on Faculty Psychology*. Cambridge, Mass.: MIT Press. French translation: *La modularité de l'esprit: essai sur la psychologie des facultés*. Paris: Éditions de Minuit, 1986.

Forster K.I. (1979). Levels of processing and the structure of language. In: W.E. Cooper and E.C.T. Walker (Eds.), *Sentence Processing: Psycholinguistics Studies Presented to Merrill Garrett*. Hillsdale, N.J.: Lawrence Erlbaum Associates, pp. 27-85.

Foundas A.L., Faulbhader J.R., Kulynych J.J., Browning C.A. and Weinberger D.R. (1999). Hemispheric and sex-linked differences in Sylvian fissure morphology: a quantitative approach using volumetric magnetic resonance imaging. *Neuropsychiatry Neuropsychology Behavioral Neurology*, **12(1)**: 1-10.

Frederikse M.E., Lu A., Aylward E., Barta P. and Pearlson G. (1999). Sex differences in the inferior parietal lobule. *Cerebral Cortex*, **9(8)**: 896-901.

Friederici A.D. (2002). Towards a neural basis of auditory sentence processing. *Trends in Cognitive Sciences*, **6(2)**: 78-84.

Friederici A.D., Meyer M. and Von Cramon D.Y. (2000). Auditory language comprehension: an event related fRMI study on the processing of syntactic and lexical information. *Brain and Language*, **74:** 289-300.

Friederici A.D., Rüschemeyer S.A., Hahne A. and Fiebach C.J. (2003). The role of left inferior frontal and superior temporal cortex in sentence comprehension: localizing syntactic and semantic processes. *Cerebral Cortex*, **13:** 170-177.

Friedrich F.J., Egly R., Rafal R.D. and Beck D. (1998). Spatial attention deficits in humans: a comparison of superior parietal and temporo-parietal junction lesions. *Neuropsychology*, **12(2):** 193-207.

Geary D.C. (1998). *Male, Female: The Evolution of Human Sex Differences.* Washington, DC: American Psychological Association, pp. 397.

George N., Evans J.-J., Fiori N., Davidoff J. and Renault B. (1996). Brain events related to normal and moderately scrambled faces. *Cognitive Brain Research*, **4:** 65-76.

George N., Jemel B., Fiori N. and Renault B. (1997). Face and shape repetition effects in humans: a spatio-temporal ERP study. *NeuroReport*, **6:** 1417-1423.

George N., Jemel B., Fiori N., Chaby L. and Renault B. (2005). Electrophysiological correlates of facial decision: Insights from upright and upside-down Mooney-face perception. *Cognitive Brain Research*, **24:** 663-673.

Geschwind N. and Levitsky W. (1968). Human-brain: left-right asymmetries in temporal speech region. *Science*, **161:** 186-187.

Gevins A.S. and Cutillo B.C. (1986). Signals of cognition. In: F. Lopes da Silva, W. Storm van Leeuwen and A. Remond (Eds.), *Handbook of Electroencephalography and Clinical Neurophysiology*, Vol. 2: *Clinical Applications of Computer Analysis of EEG and other Neurophysiological Signals*, Amsterdam: Elsevier, pp. 335-381.

Giard M.H., Perrin F., Pernier J. and Bouchet P. (1990). Brain generators implicated in the processing of auditory stimulus deviance: A topographic ERP study. *Psychophysiology*, **27:** 627-640.

Goldman-Rakic P. (1992). Mémoire et pensée. *Pour la Science*, **181:** 88-97.

Goldman-Rakic P. (1997). Space and time in the mental universe. *Nature*, **386:** 589-590.

Goodale M.A. and Milner D.A. (1992). Separate visual pathways for perception and action. *Trends in Neurosciences*, **15:** 20-25.

Grafton S., Hazeltin E. and Ivry R. (1995). Functional mapping of sequence learning in normal humans. *Journal of Cognitive Neurosciences*, **7:** 497-510.

Gross C.G., Rocha-Miranda C.E. and Bender D.B. (1972). Visual properties in inferotemporal cortex of the macaque. *Journal of Neurophysiology*, **35(1)**: 96-111.

Gur R.C., Turketsky B.I., Matsui M., Yan M., Bilker W., Hughett P. and Gur R.E. (1999). Sex differences in brain gray and white matter in healthy young adults: correlations with cognitive performance. *Journal of Neuroscience*, **19(10)**: 4065-4072.

Halgren E. (1988). The P3: A view from the brain. *Behavioral Brain Science*, **11**: 383-385.

Hall J.A. (1984). *Non-verbal Sex Differences: Communication Accuracy and Expressive Style*. Baltimore, MD: John Hopkins University Press.

Harasty J., Double K.L., Halliday G.M., Kril J.J. and McRitchie (1997). Language-associated cortical regions are proportionally larger in the female brain. *Arch. Neurol.*, **54(2)**: 171-176.

Hasselmo M.E., Rolls E.T. and Baylis G.C. (1989). The role of expression and identity in the face-selective responses of neurons in the temporal visual cortex of the monkey. *Behavioral Brain Research*, **32(3)**: 203-218.

Haxby J.V., Grady C., Horwitz B., Ungerleider L.G., Mishkin M., Carson R.E., Herscovitch P., Schapiro M.B. and Rapoport S. (1991). Dissociation of object and spatial visual processing pathways in human extrastriate cortex. *Proceedings of National Academy of Sciences of the USA*, **88**: 1621-1625.

Haxby J.V., Hoffman E.A., and Gobbini M.I. (2000). The distributed neural system for face perception. *Trends in Cognitive Sciences*, **4**: 223-233.

Haxby J.V., Gobbin M.I., Furey M.L., Ishai A., Schouten J.L. and Pietrini P. (2001). Distributed and overlapping representations of faces and objects in ventral temporal cortex. *Science*, **293**: 2425-2430.

Hebb D. (1948). *The Organization of Behavior: A Neuropsychological Theory*. New York: Wiley.

Hécaen H. (1972). *Introduction à la Neuropsychologie*. Paris: Larousse.

Heinze H.J., Mangun G.R., Burchert W., Hinrichis H., Johannes S., Hundershagen H., Gazzaniga M.S. and Hillyard S.A. (1994). Combined spatial and temporal imaging of brain activity during visual selective attention in humans. *Nature*, **372**: 543-546.

Hillyard S.A., Hink R.F., Shwent V.L. and Picton T.W. (1973). Electrical signs of selective attention in the human brain. *Science*, **182**: 177-180.

Hillyard S.A. and Anllo-Vento L. (1998). Event-related brain potentials in the study of visual selective attention. *Proceedings of National Academy of Sciences of the USA*, **95(3)**: 781-787.

Homa D., Haver B. and Schwartz T. (1976). Perceptibility of schematic face stimuli: evidence for a perceptual Gelstalt. *Memory and Cognition*, **4(2)**: 176-185.

Hubel D. and Wiesel T. (1962). Receptive fields, binocular interaction and. functional architecture in the cat's visual cortex. *Journal of Physiology* (London), **160**: 106-154.

Hubel D. and Wiesel T. (1968). Receptive fields and functional architecture of monkey striate cortex. *Journal of Physiology* (London), **195**: 215-243.

Hubel D. and Wiesel T. (1977). Functional architecture of the macaque monkey visual cortex. *Proceedings of the Royal Society of London.* Séries B, **198**: 1-59.

Jaeger J.J., Lockwood A.H., Van Valin R.D. Jr, Kemmerer D.L., Murphy B.W. and Wacks D.S (1998). Sex differences in brain regions activated by grammatical and reading tasks. *Neuroreport,* **9(12)**: 2803-2807.

James W. (1884). What is an emotion? *Mind,* **9**: 188-205.

Janowsky J.S., Chavez B. and Orwoll E. (2000). Sex steroids modify working memory. *Journal of Cognitive Neuroscience,* **12(3)**: 407-414.

Jemel B., George N., Olivares E., Fiori N. and Renault B. (1999). Event-related potentials evidence specific face incongruities processing. *Psychophysiology,* **36**, 437-452.

Johnson R.J. (1988). The amplitude of the P300 component of the event-related potential: Review and synthesis. *Advances in Psychophysiology,* **3**: 69-137.

Kapp B.S., Pascoe J.P. and Bixler M.A. (1984). The amygdala: a neuroanatomical systems approach to its contributions to aversive conditioning. In: N. Butler and L.R. Squire (Eds.), *Neuropsychology of Memory.* New York: Guilford.

Kapur S., Craik F.I., Tulving E., Wilson A., Houle S. and Brown G. (1994). Neuroanatomical correlates of encoding in episodic memory: levels of processing effect. *Proceedings of National Academic Sciences USA,* **91**: 2008-2011.

Kastner S., De Weerd P., Desimone R. and Ungerleider L.G. (1998). Mechanisms of directed attention in the human extrastriate cortex as revealed by functional MRI. *Science,* **282(5386)**: 108-111.

Kaufmann J.M. and Schweinberger S.R. (2004). Expression influences the recognition of familiar faces. *Perception,* **33**: 399-408.

Kim J.H., Ellman A. and Juraska J.M. (1996). A re-examination of sex differences in axon density and number in the splenium of the rat corpus callosum. *Brain Research,* **740(1-2)**: 47-56.

Kimura D. (2001). *Cerveau d'Homme, Cerveau de Femme.* Paris: Odile Jacob. Translation by D. Kimura (1999), *Sex and Cognition.* Cambridge, Mass.: Bradford Books, MIT Press.

Kinomura S., Larsson J., Gulyas B. and Roland P.E. (1996). Activation by attention of the human reticular formation and thalamic intralaminar nuclei. *Science,* **271**(5248): 512-515.

Klüver H. and Bucy P.C. (1939). Preliminary analysis of functions of the temporal lobes in monkeys. *Archives of Neurology and Psychiatry*, **42**: 979-1000.

Knowlton B.J., Mangels J.A. and Squire L.R. (1996). A neostriatal habit learning system on humans. *Science*, **273**: 1399-1402.

Kurucz J. and Feldmar G. (1979). Prosopo-affective agnosia as a symptom of cerebral organic disease. *Journal of American Geriatric Society*, **27**: 225-230.

Kutas M. and Hillyard S.A. (1980). Reading senseless sentence: Brain potentials reflect semantic incongruity. *Science*, **207**: 203-204.

La Bar K.S., Gatenby J.C., Gore J.C., Le Doux J.E. and Phelps E.A. (1998). Human amygdala activation during conditioned fear acquisition and extinction: a mixed-trial fRMI study. *Neuron*, **20**: 936-945.

LaBerge D., Auclair L. and Sieroff E. (2000). Preparatory Attention: Experiment and Theory. *Consciousness and Cognition*, **9(3)**: 396-403.

Lange C.G. (1887). *The Emotions*. Baltimore: Williams and Wilkins.

Lepage M., Habib M. and Tulving E. (1988). Hippocampal PET activations of memory encoding and retrieval: the HIPER model. *Hippocampus*, **8**: 313-322.

Lepage M., Ghaffar O., Nyberg L. and Tulving E. (2000). Prefrontal cortex and episodic memory retrieval mode. *Proceedings of the National Academy of Sciences of the USA*, **97**: 506-511.

Lewin J.S., Jonathan S., Friedman L., Wu D., Miller D.A., Thompson L.A., Klein S.K., Wise A.L., Hedera P., Buckley P., Meltzer H., Friedland R.P. and Duerk J.L. (1996). Cortical localization of human sustained attention: detection with functional MR using a visual vigilance paradigm. *Journal of Computer Assisted Tomography*, **20(5)**: 695-701.

Linn M.C. and Pertersen A.C. (1985). Emergence and characterization of sex differences in spatial ability: a meta-analysis. *Child Development*, **56**: 1479-1788.

Mandler G. (1984). *Mind and Body. Psychology of Emotion and Stress*. New York, London: WW Norton and Company.

Mangun G.R., Hillyard S.A. and Luck S. (1993). Electrocortical substrates of visual selective attention. In: D.E. Meyer and S. Kornblum (Eds.), *Attention and Performance XIV: Synergies in Experimental Psychology, Artificial Intelligence and Cognitive Neuroscience*, Cambridge, Mass.: MIT Press.

Mangun G.R., Hopfinger J.B., Kussmaul C.L., Fletcher E.M. and Heinze H.J. (1997). Covariations in ERP and PET measures of spatial selective attention in human extra-striate visual cortex. *Human Brain Mapping*, **5**: 273-279.

Marslen-Wilson W.D. (1984). Functions and process in spoken word recognition. In: H. Bouma and D.G. Bouwhuis (Eds.), *Attention and Performance X: Control of Language Processes.* Hillsdale, N.J.: Lawrence Erlbaum Associates.

McClelland J.L. (1979). On the time relations of mental processes: an examination of system of processes in cascade. *Psychological Review,* **86:** 287-331.

McLean P.D. (1955). The limbic system ("visceral brain") and emotional behavior. *Archives of Neurology and Psychiatry,* **73:** 130-134.

McNeal J.E. and Warrington E.K. (1991). Prosopagnosia: a classification. *The Quarterly Journal of Experimental Psychology,* **43A:** 267-287.

Mesulam M.M. (1990). Large-scale neurocognitive networks and distributed processing for attention, language, and memory. *Annals of Neurology,* **28(5):** 597-613.

Mooney C.M. (1957). Age in the development of closure ability in children. *Canadian Journal of Psychology,* **11(4):** 219-226.

Morton J. (1969). Interaction of information in word recognition. *Psychological Review,* **76(2):** 165-178.

Näätänen R. (1992). *Attention and Brain Function.* Hillsdale, N.J.: Lawrence Erlbaum Associates.

Näätänen R. and Gaillard A.W.K. (1983). The N2 deflection of ERP and the orienting reflex. In: A.W.K. Gaillard and W. Ritter (Eds.), *EEG Correlates of Information Processing: Theoretical Issues,* Amsterdam: North Holland, pp. 119-141.

Nobre A.C., Sebestyen G.N., Gitelman D.R., Mesulam M., Frackowiak R.S. and Frith C.D. (1997). Functional localization of the system for visuospatial attention using positron emission tomography. *Brain,* **120:** 515-533.

Nolde S.F., Johnson M.K. and Raye C.L. (1998). The role of prefrontal cortex during tests of episodic memory. *Trends in Neurosciences,* **2:** 399-406.

Nopoulos, P., Flaum M., O'Leary D. and Andreasen N.C. (2000). Sexual dimorphism in the human brain: evaluation of tissue volume, tissue composition and surface anatomy using magnetic resonance imaging. *Psychiatry Research,* **98(1):** 1-13.

Norman D.A. and Shallice T. (1986). *Attention to Action: Willed and Automatic Control of Behaviour.* Center for Human Information Processing Report 99. La Jolla, Calif.: University of California, San Diego.

Nowicka A. and Ferstein E. (2001). Sex-related interhemispheric transmission time in the human brain. *NeuroReport,* **12(18):** 4171-4175.

O'Keefe J.A. (1979). Place units in the hippocampus of the freely moving rat. *Experimental Neurology,* **51:** 78-109.

Olds J. and Milner P. (1954). Positive reinforcement produced by electrical stimulation of the spetal area and other regions of the rat brain. *Journal of Comparative Physiological Psychology*, **47**: 419-427.

Pardo J.V., Fox P.T. and Raichle M.E. (1991). Localization of a human system for sustained attention by positron emission tomography. *Nature*, **349**: 61-63.

— Cerebral lateralization at different stages of facial processing. *Cortex*, **23**: 99-110.

— (1998). Processing syntactic relations in language and music: an event-related potential study. *Journal of Cognitive Neuroscience*, **10**: 717-733.

Pease A. and Pease B. (1989). *Pourquoi les hommes n'écoutent jamais rien et les femmes ne savent pas lire les cartes routières*. First Édition, collection "Savoir pour agir".

Perret D.I., Rolls E.T. and Cann W. (1982). Visual neurones responsive of faces in the monkey temporal cortex. *Experimental Brain Research*, **47**: 329-342.

Perret D.I., Smith P.A.J., Mistlin A.J., Chitty A.J., Head A.S., Potter D.D., Broennimann R., Milner A.D. and Jeeves M.A. (1985). Visual analysis of body movements by neurones in the temporal cortex of the macaque monkey: a preliminary report. *Behavioral Brain Research*, **16**: 153-170.

Perret D.I., Mistlin A.J. and Chitty A.J. (1987). Visual neurones responsive to faces. *Trends in Neurosciences*, **10(9)**: 358-364.

Perry R.F. and Zecki S. (2000). The neurology of saccades and covert shifts of spatial attention. *Brain*, **123**: 2273-2293.

Petersen S.E. and Fiez J.A. (1993). The processing of single words studies with positron emission. *Annual Review of Neuroscience*, **16**: 509-530.

Petersen S.E., Fox P.T., Snyder A.Z. and Raichle M.E. (1990). Activation of extrastriate and frontal cortical areas by visual words and word-like stimuli. *Science*, **249**: 1041-1044.

Posner M.I. and Raichle M.E. (1994). *Images of Mind*. New York, W.H. Freeman (French translation: *L'Esprit en Images*, 1998: Paris, De Boeck Université).

Pugh K.R., Offywitz BA, Shaywitz S.A., Fullbright R.K., Byrd D., Skudlarski P., Shankweiler S.E., Katz L., Constable R.T., Fletcher J., Lacadie C., Marchione K. and Gore J.C. (1996). Auditory selective attention: an fMRI inverstigation. *NeuroImage*, **4(3)**: 159-173.

Renault B., Signoret J.L., Debruille B., Breton F. and Bolger F. (1989). Brain potentials reveal covert facial recognition in prosopagnosia. *Neuropsychologia*, **27(7)**: 905-912.

Rosenthal R., Hall J.A., Dimatteo M.R., Rogers P.L. and Archer D. (1979). *Sensitivity to Nonverbal Communication: The PONS Test*. Baltimore: Johns Hopkins University Press.

Sansone S. and Tiberghien G. (1994). Traitement de l'expression faciale et reconnaisance des visages. *Psychologie Française*, **39**: 327-344.

Schachter S. (1964). The interaction of cognitive and physiological determinants of emotional state. *Advances in Experimental Social Psychology*, **1**: 49-80.

Segui J. (1998). Langage. In: O. Houdé, D. Kayser, O. Koenig, J. Proust and F. Rastier (Eds.), *Vocabulaire de Sciences Cognitives*. PUF, Psychologie et Sciences de la Pensée.

Selye H. (1956). *Le Stress de la Vie.* Gallimard.

Sergent J. and Signoret J.L. (1992). Functional and anatomical decomposition of face processing: evidence from prosopagnosia and PET study of normal subjects. *Philosophical Transactions of the Royal Society of London,* Series B, **335**: 55-62.

Sergent J., Ohta S., McDonald B. and Zuck E. (1994). Segregated processing of facial identity and emotion in the human brain: a PET study. *Visual Cognition,* **1(2)**: 349-369.

Sieroff E. (2004). *La Neuropsychologie: Approche Cognitive des Syndromes Cliniques.* Paris: Armand Colin, coll. "Cursus".

Squire L.R. (1987). *Memory and Brain.* New York: Oxford University Press.

Squire L.R., Ojeman J.G., Miezin F.S., Petersen S.E., Videen T.O. and Raichle M.E. (1992). Activation of the hippocampus in normal humans: A functional anatomical study of memory. *Proceedings of National Academy of Sciences of the USA,* **89**: 1837-1841.

Steinmetz H., Staiger J.F., Schlaug G., Huang Y. and Jancke L. (1995). Corpus callosum and brain volume in women and me. *NeuroReport,* **6(7)**: 1002-1004.

Stroop J. (1935). Studies of interference in serial verbal reaction. *Experimental Psychology,* **18**: 643-662.

Sutton S., Barren M., Zubin J. and John E.R. (1965). Evoked potentials correlates of stimulation uncertainty. *Science,* **150**: 1187-1188.

Tanaka J.W. and Farah M.J. (1993). Parts and wholes in face recognition. *The Quarterly Journal of Experimental Psychology,* **46A(2)**: 225-245.

Taylor S.F., Kornblum S., Lauber E.J., Minoshima S. and Koeppe R.A. (1997). Isolation of specific interference processing in the Stroop task: PET activation studies. *NeuroImage,* **6(2)**: 81-92.

Thompson P. (1980). Margaret Thatcher: a new illusion. *Perception,* **9**: 483-484.

Treisman A.M. (1960). Contextual cues in selective listening. *Quarterly Journal of Experimental Psychology,* **12**: 242-248.

Tulving E. (1972). Episodic and semantic memory. In: E. Tulving and W. Donaldson (Eds.), *Organization of Memory*, pp. 381-403. New York: Academic Press.

Tulving E. and Schachter D.L. (1990). Priming and human memory systems. *Science*, **247**: 301-306.

Tulving E., Kapur S., Craik F.I., Moscovitch M. and Houle S. (1994). Hemispheric encoding/retrieval asymmetry in episodic memory: positron emission tomography findings. *Proceedings of the National Academy of Sciences of the USA*, **91**: 2015-2020.

Tzourio-Mazoyer N., Josse G., Crivello F. and Mazoyer B. (2004). Interindividual variability in the hemispheric organization for speech. *NeuroImage*, **21**: 422-435.

Ungerleider L.G. and Mishkin M. (1982). Two cortical visual systems. In: D.J. Engle, M.A. Goodale and R.J. Mansfield (Eds.), *Analysis of Visual Behaviour*, Cambridge, Mass.: MIT Press.

Valentine T. (1988). Upside-down faces: a review of the effect of inversion upon faces recognition. *British Journal of Psychology*, **79**: 471-491.

Vanderbergue R., Duncan J., Dupont P., Ward R., Poline J.B., Bormans G., Michiels J., Montelmans L. and Orban G.A. (1997). Attention to 1 or 2 features in left-or-right visual fields: a positron emission tomography study. *Journal of Neuroscience*, **17(10)**: 3739-3750.

Van Rullen and Thorpe (2001). The time course of visual processing: from early perception to decision-making. *Journal of Cognitive Neuroscience*, **13(4)**: 454-461.

Voyer D., Voyer S. and Bryden M.P. (1995). Magnitude of sex differences in spatial abilities: a meta-analysis and consideration of critical variables. *Psychological Bulletin*, **117**: 250-270.

Vuillemier P., Armony J.L., Driver J. and Dolan R. (2003). Distinct spatial frequency sensitivities for processing faces and emotional expressions. *Nature Neurosciences*, **6(6)**: 624: 631.

Wada J. and Rasmussen T. (1960). Intracarotid injection of sodium Amytal for the lateralization of cerebral speech dominance: Experimental and clinical observations. *Journal of Neurosurgery*, **17**: 266-282.

Wagner H.L., Buck R. and Winterbotham M. (1993). Communication of specific emotions: Gender differences in sending accuracy and communication measures? *Journal of Nonverbal Behavior*, **17**: 29-53.

Walter W.G., Cooper R., Aldridge V.J., McCallum C. and Winter A.L. (1964). Contingent negative variation: An electrical sign of sensori-motor association and expectancy in the human brain. *Nature*, **26**: 529-547.

Warren C. and Morton J. (1982). The effects of priming on picture recognition. *British Journal of Psychology*, **73**: 117-129.

Yin R.K. (1969). Looking at upside-down faces. *Journal of Experimental Psychology*, **81(1)**: 141-145.

Yin R.K. (1970). Face-recognition by brain-injured patients: a dissociable ability? *Neuropsychologia*, **8**: 395-402.

Young A.W., Hellawell D.J., Van de Wall C. and Johnson M. (1996). Facial expression processing after amygdalotomy. *Neuropsychologia*, **34(1)**: 31-39.

Zihl J., Von Cramon D. and Mai N. (1983). Selective disturbance of movement vision after bilateral brain damage. *Brain*, **106**: 313-340.

Zola-Morgan S., Squire L.R. and Amaral D.G. (1986). Human amnesia and the medial temporal region: enduring memory impairment following a bilateral lesion limited to field CA1 of the hippocampus. *Journal of Neuroscience*, **6**: 2950-2967.

Index

Action potential, 15-18, 33, 53-54, 91
Alzheimer's disease, 8, 85, 87
Amnesia
    anterograde, 81, 82, 86
    diencephalic, 86
    retrograde, 81, 84, 85, 86
Amygdala, 21, 23, 24, 82, 86, 139-141, 142, 147-148
Amygdalo-thalamo-cingular circuit, 86-87
Anterior commissure, 21, 131
Aphasia
    Broca's, 6, 97-98, 107
    conduction, 98-99
    male/female differences, 130-131
    Wernicke's, 6, 98
Areas
    associative, 22, 49, 56, 58, 82, 85, 92, 104, 125-126, 145-146
    Broca's, 96-99, 106, 107-108, 109, 122, 130-131, 143, 145
    Brodmann, 31, 56, 58, 65, 89, 98, 103, 120, 145
    primary, 22, 49, 57, 126
    secondary, 58
    visual, 21, 22, 37, 56-58, 61, 90, 148
    Wernicke's, 97, 108, 123, 131
Asymmetry, 90, 96, 109, 122, 123, 131

Attention, 116
    attentional filtering, 120
    disengagement, 113, 119
    effect, 116
    orientation, 75, 112-115, 118-119
    Posner and Raichle model, 112
    return inhibition, 112-113
    selective, 110, 115-116, 120
    visuo-spatial, 112-113, 117, 119, 132
Automatic processes, 103, 117
Autonomous nervous system, 28
    parasympathetic, 28
    sympathetic, 29

Basal ganglia, 87-88, 104, 107, 141
BOLD (response), 47
Brain imaging, 73, 114
    experiments using, 62, 83, 140
    methods, 32-33, 95
Broca, 6, 33, 95-96, 98, 106-107, 109, 123, 130, 138, 144
Brodmann (areas) [see Areas (Brodmann)]
Bulb, 25

Callous body, 7, 21, 23, 98-99, 126, 130-131, 138